Cutting
and Styling

Cutting and Styling

SECOND EDITION

LESLEY ELLIS

LONGMAN

Addison Wesley Longman

Addison Wesley Longman Limited,
Edinburgh Gate, Harlow,
Essex CM20 2JE, England
and associated companies throughout the world

First published 1987 by Blackwell Scientific Publications Ltd
Reprinted 1989
Reprinted with minor amendments 1991
Reprinted by Longman Group Ltd 1995

This edition 1997

British Library Cataloguing in Publication Data
A catalogue entry for this title is available from the British Library

ISBN 0-582-31047-4

Set by 30 in 10/12 Palatino

Produced by Longman Singapore Publishers (Pte) Ltd
Printed in Singapore

Contents

About this Book

This second edition has been updated to cover the skills needed by those taking hairdressing qualifications at NVQ/SVQ levels 1–3. It is written in a direct and easy to follow style and is essential for those beginning their hairdressing career and as a practical guide and inspiration for the more experienced stylist or teacher.

There are short revision questions at the end of each chapter for you to test how much you have learnt (all the answers are in the text!) plus a selection of more challenging questions for experienced stylists. The glossary at the end of the book will serve as a quick reference guide to those words which may be new to you or to terminology you may have forgotten.

The top hairdressers are those who have a thorough understanding of the theoretical aspects of their craft which underpins their practical skills. This book will help you to become one of these people.

The book assumes a basic level of knowledge and omits subjects that are not strictly related to cutting and styling.

Acknowledgements

I would like to thank the following individuals and organisations who kindly contributed to this book:

Antenna, London
BaByliss Ltd
Cheynes, Edinburgh
Goldwell
House of Carmen Ltd
Becky and Nick Cronin of 'Loco Design'
L'Oréal Technical Centre, London
Molton Brown, London
Pietranera (UK) Ltd
Rand Rocket Ltd
Rencene Ltd
Vidal Sassoon, London
Trevor Sorbie, London
Verelle Hairdressing, Fareham
Wahl Ltd
Wella (GB) Ltd

Last, but by no means least, I would like to thank my husband, Keith Ellis, who is always a pillar of strength and gave me support when it was most needed.

Lesley Ellis

Chapter 1

BASIC FACTS

Introduction

The first thing that all hairdressers need to know about is the hair they are dealing with every day of their working lives. Every head of hair you handle will both look and feel different – why? This chapter is intended to provide you with fundamental knowledge of the different types of hair, how a hair grows, its structure, characteristics, properties and the effects of products on hair.

Hair facts

What is hair?

Hair is composed of a type of protein, called *keratin*, which is different from other proteins because it contains sulphur. The chemical composition of hair is shown in Figure 1.1. There are *three* different types of hair found on the human body:

- *Lanugo* hair is found on the human foetus before birth
- *Vellus* hair is the fine downy hair found all over our bodies, except the soles of our feet, palms of our hands, and lips. (Yes, there are even hairs on our eyelids.)
- *Terminal* hair is coarser and is the type of hair that we deal with as hairdressers. It is coarser than vellus hair and is found on the scalp, on men's faces, under the arms and in the pubic region.

Figure 1.1 Chemical composition of hair

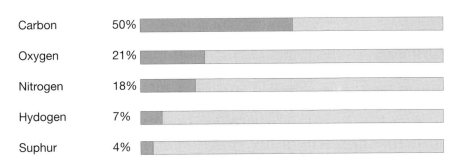

Carbon	50%
Oxygen	21%
Nitrogen	18%
Hydogen	7%
Suphur	4%

Hair can be classified into the following *ethnic* types:

- Afro-Caribbean/Negroid
- Chinese/Mongolian
- European/Caucasian

You will already be aware that hair also differs in texture and density. We use certain words to define these differences in the appearance and feel of hair. We describe the texture of hair with the use of words like curly, straight, thick, fine, coarse, and so on, while the density of the hair (i.e. how many hairs there are on the scalp) is described as thick, thin/fine, dense, sparse, etc. Natural redheads have about 90,000 hairs on their heads, while natural blondes have about 140,000 and brunettes fall somewhere in between. Therefore, natural blondes appear to have the most dense hair but also tend to have the finest (smallest in diameter) hair. Incidentally, female hair is usually finer than male hair.

We also use words to describe the condition of a client's hair. Such words include dry, porous, sensitised, damaged, brittle, resistant, and so on.

As the fibre we are dealing with is dead, there is nothing we can do to change the way it grows. Cutting hair will not make it grow faster or thicker. Once hair has been damaged, it cannot be permanently restored to its original condition. The only way to change the quality for new hair is through diet and good haircare routines.

How does a hair grow?

All hairs grow from a minute pit in the skin surface called a hair *follicle*. The number of hair follicles we have is determined through our genes and does not alter throughout our lives. However, whether a hair grows out from the follicle, and the type of hair produced from it will change. For example, the vellus hair on a young boy's face alters as he reaches maturity to become terminal hair and where terminal hair was once in profusion on his scalp may be replaced by vellus hairs (male pattern baldness). The hairs we see emerging from these follicles is dead but at the base of the follicle the hair is alive and actively growing. There is a lot of activity at the base of the follicle and this area is called the *papilla*. It is here that cells are dividing and subdividing to produce hair as we recognise it. As the cells are going through this dividing process (called *mitosis*) there is nowhere else for them to go than up the follicle channel towards the opening on the skin's surface. As the hair is forming and making its way up the follicle, it changes from being a soft,. pulpy mass, to becoming harder and, by the time it emerges, hair as we know it. It is at the papilla that the hair's colour and shape is determined. Cells called *melanocytes* give the hair cells pigment which determines the hair's natural colour. When these melanocytes stop working, the hair from that particular follicle will emerge white or, technically speaking, colourless. The papilla is able to do all this work because it is nourished by a constant source of food and oxygen via a network of blood capillaries. Therefore, if a person's diet is lacking in certain vitamins or the blood is intoxicated with chemicals, the hair will suffer. An example of this happening is when certain chemotherapy treatments, used for combating illnesses such as cancer, cause patients to lose their hair. The 'slimming disease' anorexia nervosa also provides evidence that if the papilla is starved of the nutrients needed, the hair may temporarily cease to grow normally. Hormones, transported around our bodies by our blood, also affect hair growth. It is hormones which cause hairs to change from vellus to terminal hair and vice versa and it is not uncommon for women to experience slight hair loss following childbirth as a result of such a sudden change to their hormonal balance.

Hair grows approximately 1.25 cm (about half an inch) on average per month but tends to grow slightly quicker during the summer months. On average, we lose about sixty hairs a day. These are shed naturally when we comb, brush or shampoo our hair. The reason we lose some hairs but not all in one go (unless something is very wrong) is because we have a hair growth cycle. About 85 per cent of the hairs on your head are actively growing and these hairs are described as being in the *anagen* stage of the growth cycle. The anagen stage can last up to seven years, although it is more common to last two to three years. Once the individual hair has stopped growing, it will reach the *catagen* stage. This is when the hair is dying and comes away from the base of the follicle and therefore its source of growth. About 1 per cent of the hairs on our heads are in the catagen stage, which lasts about two weeks. The follicle then rests for about three or four months and this is called the *telogen* stage. About 14 per cent of our hairs are in this resting stage at any time. Following this rest, a new hair starts to grow and anagen starts again. This is shown in Figure 1.2.

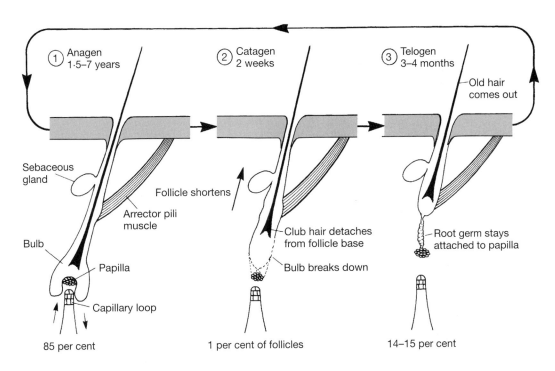

Figure 1.2 The growth cycle of hair

Note: remember the three stages of hair growth by 'ACT' and think of the three stages as

Active   Collapsing   Tired

To remember the hair growth cycle stages, use the word ACT to help commit it to memory:

A = Anagen
C = Catagen
T = Telogen

What is the structure of hair like?

Hair is made up of three layers and can be likened to a pencil. The outside of the hair (the paint on a pencil) is called the *cuticle* and provides protection for the layers below. The next layer makes up the bulk of the hair (the wood of the pencil) and is called the *cortex*. The centre layer (the lead of the pencil) is called the *medulla*.

Figure 1.3 shows a hair which has been magnified over one thousand times. It would be impossible to see this detail with the naked eye. The scales you can see are one of several layers which is called the *cuticle*. European hair has about seven layers of these scales. Chinese hair has as many as eleven layers while Afro-Caribbean hair the fewest layers. The cuticle is completely colourless and the scales overlap each other rather like the scales on a fish. The cuticle protects the hair; when it is lying flat and smooth, it is responsible for making the hair shine because it reflects light. When the cuticle becomes damaged and worn, the scales will be open and rough and the hair will appear dull because light is refracted. A cuticle in this damaged state is referred to as being *porous*. The cuticle scales are translucent, which means they allow some light to pass through them. The colour we see is in the layer below the cuticle; we see the colour because of the cuticle's translucency.

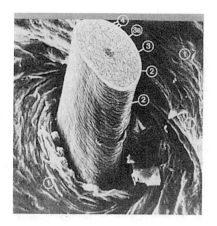

Figure 1.3 A magnified hair
The hair shaft emerges from the scalp, showing
1 The horny layer of epidermis which can be seen around the follicle opening
2 The cuticle, showing the various overlapping layers of scales
3 The columnar cortical cells that contain granules of pigment
3a The medulla, a series of air spaces in the centre of the hair
4 The intracellular cement that surrounds the cortical fibres
(Courtesy Wella Ltd)

The layer below the cuticle is called the *cortex*, which makes up the bulk of a hair. The cortex, protected by the cuticle, is responsible for giving a hair its strength and elasticity and contains the natural pigment. The cortical fibres are rather like a bunch of straws held together by complex bonds.

Cross-linkages of hair

There are three types of cross-linkages in the keratin of hair, illustrated in Figure 1.4.

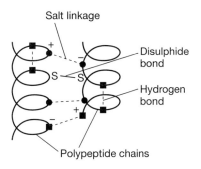

Disulphide linkages

These are the most important bonds as far as perming and straightening are concerned as it is these that are broken to allow the alteration of the hair shape. The amino acid cystine forms a link through its central disulphide bond between two adjacent polypeptide chains. The cystine or disulphide linkages are like the rungs of a ladder. These are very strong bonds which can be broken only by chemicals.

Average hair contains 4–5 per cent sulphur, but natural red hair may contain up to 8 per cent sulphur. Because this is almost twice as much as in normal hair, red hair, with its higher sulphur content, is more resistant and difficult to perm.

Salt linkages

The amino acids that form polypeptides may have free acid (negative) or basic amino (positive) groups. If a free negative charge in one polypeptide chain lies opposite a free positive charge in an adjacent chain there will be an attraction between them. Opposite electrical charges attract, rather like the North and South poles of a magnet. These salt linkages are also called ionic or electrostatic charges. Because they are weaker than the disulphide linkages they can be easily broken by weak acids or alkalis. If you quickly run a nylon comb through your hair for a minute it will be able to attract and pick up a small piece of paper. The comb has picked up a charge from the hair and the opposite charge induced in the piece of paper attracts the two together. This is an example of an electrostatic charge.

Hydrogen bonds

These weak bonds are due to the attraction between hydrogen atoms and oxygen atoms (like the salt linkage this is an electrostatic attraction). This can occur in a polypeptide chain (between the coils) or between adjacent polypeptide chains. Since they form cross-bonds, they help the disulphide bonds to keep adjacent polypeptide chains together, giving 'body' to the hair. Although the hydrogen bonds are very weak, many more of them are present than any other bond in the hair. They can be broken by water and most weak chemicals, and will be discussed fully in Chapters 5 and 6.

The cortex is where all chemical processes take place, such as bleaches, tints, perms and relaxers. When a hair is in good condition, it is capable of being stretched up to one-third of its own length when wet without breaking and then return to its original length. If the cortex becomes damaged, the hair may break when stretched and will be weak and lifeless and lack bounce.

The natural pigment found in the cortex is deposited by the melanocytes while the hair forms at the base of the follicle. Melanocytes produce two types of pigment called *melanin* and *pheomelanin*. All natural hair colours are a combination of these two pigments. The differing amounts of these pigments result in the variations of natural hair colour we see about us. The centre of the hair is the *medulla*. The medulla serves no useful purpose to the hairdresser. It is basically an air space, which may, or may not, be continuous throughout the length of a hair. In fine hair, the medulla may be non-existent while in other hairs there may be two!

What is pH?

The term pH is simply a way of indicating how acid or alkaline something is: pH is expressed on a scale from 0 to 14, with 7.0 in the middle being the neutral point, where something is neither acid or alkaline. A simple pH scale is shown in Figure 1.5.

Figure 1.5 pH chart showing how hairdressing chemicals affect the hair

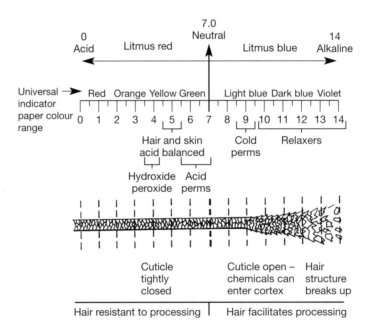

Why is pH important?

pH is important because of the way it affects the hair. Acids close (remember *c* for close) the cuticle of the hair, leaving it shiny and manageable. The natural pH of the skin and hair ranges between 4.5 and 5.5: this pH reading inhibits the growth of bacteria. Hair in its acid state resists processing. Alkaline chemicals open the cuticle of the hair and cause the hair shaft to swell. This is important to allow the entry of chemicals into the cortex (tints, bleaches and cold perms.) Hair in an alkaline state will facilitate processing. However, a high pH (usually above 10) can destroy the structure of hair. Such chemicals are called depilatories and are sold to remove unwanted hair on legs and other parts of the body.

What is a 'pH-balanced' product?

This is simply a product that has the same pH as the hair and skin, approximately 5. Such products will not upset the natural pH. After many alkaline hairdressing treatments, acid rinses are used to bring the pH back to its normal level.

How do I test pH?

One way is to use litmus, which will be red in acids and blue in alkalis. Litmus is available as paper or a liquid. It has the disadvantage that it can only tell you if a chemical is acid or alkaline, not how weak or strong it is. The second way is to use uiniversal indicator, and this changes over a range of colours corresponding to different pHs. The colour is simply matched up to a chart. Universal indicator is available as paper or liquid.

Styling products

Styling products are generally applied to wet hair and not rinsed out. They are products which are intended to maintain the hairstyle and have the following effects:

1 They contain film-forming polymers which provide a sheath of film on each strand after the hair is dried. Although the film must, to a certain degree, be flexible, it slows down the hair returning to its original shape.
2 The film on the hair helps retard the hair's ability of absorbing atmospheric moisture which would cause the hair to return to its original shape (alpha-keratin). Hair is hygroscopic which means it has a tendency to absorb moisture present in the atmosphere. If hair is subjected to humidity, the hair will return to alpha-keratin.
3 The polymers have a stiffening effect on the hair making the hairs 'weld' together. This action improves the hair's resistance to deformation.

Setting lotions

The most commonly used form of setting aid is a setting lotion, which is generally supplied in individual application bottles. Setting lotions are available in different formulae designed to give gentle hold or maximum hold. Also, setting lotions may contain colour to add temporary colour to a person's hair. The lotions which contain colour are often referred to as 'rinses' or simply 'coloured lotions'.

Setting lotions prevent the hair from drying out too quickly during setting and also help to prolong the life of the set by excluding atmospheric moisture from the hair shaft. There are historically two types of setting lotions, those older ones based on gums and the more modern plastic setting lotions.

The gums were obtained when trees were damaged, as an exudation from the wounded bark. The two best-known ones are gum tragacanth (Turkish) and gum karaya (Indian). When added to a solution of water and alcohol the gums form a sticky solution called a mucilage. Their use is now obsolete because they yielded dull, brittle films, which crumbled into dust and became sticky in humid air because they were hygroscopic.

The modern setting lotions that you use in the salons contain plastic resins and polymers dissolved in a mixture of alcohol and water. The plastic resin is left as a flexible covering film on the hair when the water and alcohol have evaporated. They may contain resins or polymers such as polyvinyl pyrrolidone (PVP), polyvinyl acetate (PVA) or dimethylhydantoin formaldehyde resin (DMHF). Because PVP by itself is too hygroscopic, a copolymer of PVP and PVA is used in a ratio of 6:4; it is known as PVP-VA. To counteract any hardness of the plastic film, plasticisers are added. These are usually polyethyleneglycols and silicones. They make the film more flexible and water-resistant.

Setting lotions may also contain ingredients which are added to give the hair body and increased manageability. Plastic setting lotions intended for blow-drying often contain silicone oils; these lessen friction when brushing, by smoothing the cuticle of the hair, and reduce heat damage as they are heat-resistant. Conditioners, such as protein hydrolysates, are often added. Some setting lotions are available as temporary colours, containing acid dyes.

Mousses

Mousses are certainly the most popular styling aids of the 1990s. They are similar to setting lotions and hairsprays as far as ingredients are concerned, containing a solution of resins (polymers) and conditioning agents (silicone oils) in a mixture of water and alcohol in a pressurised container. The contents are dispensed in the form of a foam. Like hairsprays, the containers can explode if they become too hot, and the contents are flammable. Care should be taken near infra red driers or even when smoking because of this.

Mousse is available in different strengths to give increased holding power and the addition of azo dyes has made it available in different temporary colours. It is usually applied to damp hair, although it may be applied to dry hair to increase curl and texture for scrunched looks.

Mousse can be revitalised the following day after application by running wet fingers or a wet brush against the direction of the finished look before final arrangement. Try different brands to see which one you like best. Some may be more greasy than others, depending on their exact formulations.

Gels

The popularity of hair gels has diminished with the advent of a broader range of mousses, which are firmer holding. Originally, gels were preferred by many stylists because of their holding power. In hairdressing terms, the two main types of gels available are: those which cannot be seen on the hair once it is dried, and those which create a wet look, just right for sleeked back styles. They can have added ingredients which make them fluoresce or glow in the dark – ideal to be seen on a bike at night! Modern gels contain water-soluble plastic resins with a plasticiser to allow flexibility, although some preparations are deliberately made to make the hair stiff and unnatural-looking (punk styles, for example). Some clear gels are oil-in-water emulsions where tiny microscopic particles of oil are dispersed in water, to give a less greasy feel than ordinary oil-in-water emulsions. They are sometimes called micro-gels.

Some styling products are applied to the hair after it has been dried as in the case of hairsprays which provide an invisible 'hair net' to protect the hair from humidity and mechanical deformation. Other 'finishing' products include those to reduce static electricity, create manage- ability and shine, and to create texture and separation.

Dressing creams, brilliantines and serum

Dressing creams, brilliantines and serum are applied after the hair has been dried to replace the hair's natural oils. They help preserve the style by preventing the hair from absorbing atmospheric moisture and impart a sheen and lustre to the hair. They also reduce static electricity, but applying too much will make the hair lank and greasy. These products are usually based on mineral oils (classified as petroleum products) such as liquid paraffin, paraffin oil, paraffin wax and petroleum jelly (Vaseline) or vegetable oils such as castor oil and almond oil but may also contain traces of protein.

Oil sheen sprays

Oil sheen sprays are sprayed onto the hair during or after dressing the hair and are used for the same reasons as control creams and brilliantines. These must also be used sparingly to avoid the hair becoming lank and greasy and are usually sprayed at a distance of 30 cm (12 inches) from the hair. A typical oil sheen spray would contain castor oil which is dissolved in an alcohol such as industrial methylated spirit.

Revision Questions

1 What is the name of the protein of which hair is composed?

2 Name the three types of hair found on the human body.

3 Where is hair not present on the human body?

4 What are the ethnic classifications for hair?

5 What is the name of the pit in the skin's surface where a hair emerges?

6 Where is the papilla?

7 What is mitosis?

8 What are the cells called which are responsible for giving hair its colour?

9 On average, how much does hair grow in a month?

10 What are the three stages of the hair growth cycle called?

11 What are the three layers of a hair?

12 Which layer of the hair is responsible for its strength and elasticity?

13 Which layer of the hair is responsible for giving hair protection and shine?

14 Which bonds in the cortex are broken when the hair is wetted?

15 What number on the pH scale indicates neutral?

16 What is a pH-balanced product?

Advanced Questions

1 Describe the structure of hair and include a labelled diagram to show the different layers.

2 Describe how a hair is formed and grows, including:

   (i) an explanation of mitosis

   (ii) the stages of the hair growth cycle

   (iii) rate of growth and factors which affect growth

   (iv) natural pigment

3 Explain the relevance of pH-balanced products and the effect of pH on the hair.

4 Select three types of styling products and write a statement for each which covers:

   (i) the main ingredients of the product

   (ii) for what purpose the product is used.

Chapter 2

TOOLS AND EQUIPMENT

Introduction

This chapter covers the fixtures, tools and equipment that you are likely to encounter in the salon and explains how, and when to use them. It is appropriate to mention here that there are regulations which cover equipment used at work. The Provision and Use of Work Equipment Regulations (1992) impose upon the employer the duty to select equipment for use at work which is properly constructed, suitable for the purpose and kept in good repair. Employers must also ensure that all those who use the equipment have been properly trained.

Electrical appliances

All electrical appliances that are used in a salon should have a British Standards number to show that they meet minimum safety requirements. Never use an appliance with wet hands, nor if it has a cracked plug or damaged cable. *If there is an accident it is the salon owner who will be prosecuted.* If an appliance needs servicing, always disconnect from the mains and always consult an electrician if in doubt. Electricity can kill, so treat it with respect. If used properly, electric tools make the life of the hairdresser much easier.

About 200 deaths result each year as a result of electrical accidents. Obey safety rules!

Hairdriers (hand-held)

A professional hand-held drier has a much longer lifespan than an ordinary consumer model, enabling it to withstand constant daily use in salons. An example of a professional hairdrier is shown in Figure 2.1. They should be lightweight, well balanced, and have variable heat and speed controls. This enables the stylist to adjust air temperature and flow rate according to the type of hair being styled.

The flex should be long enough to enable the stylist to work easily on all sides of the head, without draping it over the client. To prevent the flex from becoming damaged the drier can be hung up on its built-in hook, so that the flex does not become twisted. When storing the drier in a bag or cupboard, always wrap the flex in a figure of eight around the handle and neck of the drier. This prevents pull on the wires inside the drier and stops

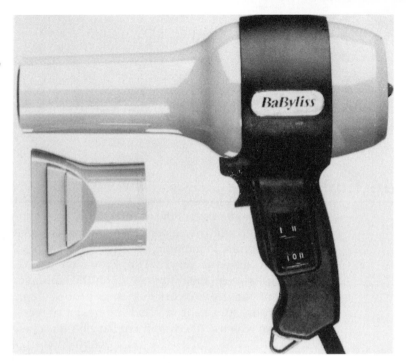

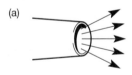

(a)

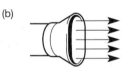

(b)

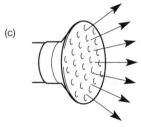

(c)

Figure 2.2 Varying airflows: (a) without a nozzle (b) with a nozzle (c) with a diffuser

the flex from becoming damaged. If the flex is wound tightly around the handle, the wires inside the flex may become brittle and fracture, causing electric shorting out. The flex will also have a tendency to coil up while you are working.

The back of these types of driers have a filter which prevents dust particles from entering the motor inside. This will require regular cleaning as a build-up of dust reduces the amount of cool air that the hairdrier can suck in, causing it to overheat and cut out. This is a safety mechanism to prevent the hairdrier from serious overheating and possibly catching fire. Disconnect the hairdrier from its socket before you clean the filter, and never work without this filter being in place, as hair could be sucked up into the fan. For this reason, a stylist with long hair should wear it tied back.

Hairdriers can be used with or without the nozzle as all this does is change the concentration of the airflow. When a nozzle is used the airflow is forced through a narrow slit which concentrates its force (see Figure 2.2b). Without a nozzle the airflow leaves the drier at a much wider angle (see Figure 2.2a).

Special attachments, called diffusers, can be bought to attach to a drier. These disperse the air at a very wide angle and are particularly useful if a style needs minimal disturbance from the airflow (see Figure 2.2c).

Safe working guide – hand-held hairdriers

- Always work with a clean filter in place.
- Never use a hairdrier if the plug is cracked or the flex is damaged.
- Never use a hairdrier with wet hands.
- Never leave cables where people could trip over them.
- Always switch a hairdrier off before putting it down. The vibration on the motor could cause it to move and fall to the ground.

- Never hold a hairdrier too close to a client's scalp. It can burn the skin and scorch the hair. For the same reason, do not play a stream of hot air on one area too long, especially if the hair has metal clips that might heat up. If you doubt this, try holding your hand near the airflow when your drier is on hot.
- For an explanation of the physical changes in hair when blow-drying or using tongs, please see Chapter 6.

Hot brushes

Hot brushes have become increasingly popular in both the professional trade and the home consumer market. Many people find them easier to handle than tongs because the hair tends to cling to the teeth. The hot brushes shown in Figure 2.3 are available in three different sizes for creating different sized curls. All hot brushes are fitted with a thermostatic control which prevents overheating. However, leaving them on all day would undoubtedly affect the lifespan of such an appliance.

Figure 2.3 A selection of hot brushes (Courtesy BaByliss Ltd)

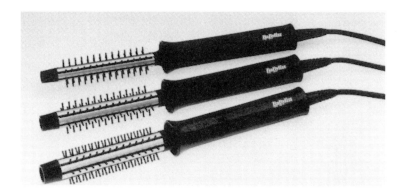

The flex of a hot brush has a swivel action so that during the turning of the brush, the flex does not twist or tangle. The points of the hair must be cleanly wrapped around the brush to prevent buckled and distorted ends. The hot brush is wound down so that the entire length of the hair is wrapped around it. Placing a comb between the hot brush and the scalp will ensure that the heat does not cause discomfort to the client. The hot brush is held in the hair for several seconds until the heat has penetrated through the mesh of hair (you can test that this has happened with your fingers). When the hair has been heated sufficiently, the hot brush is gently removed by carefully unwinding it. The hair should be allowed to cool thoroughly before it is combed or brushed.

There are hot brushes available without cords which are described as 'independent'. They use butane cartridges or batteries to provide the energy to produce heat. They are popular to take on holidays, or for hairdressers who are involved in photographic location work.

Safe working guide – hot brushes

- Do not leave hot brushes switched on longer than necessary, as this will shorten their working life and make it more likely for accidents to occur.

- Clean them regularly with the power disconnected. Use some cotton wool dampened with methylated spirit to remove dirt. Never immerse in water to clean.
- Take clean sections so that the brush does not get tangled in the hair.
- Because damaged hair cannot withstand as much heat as hair in good condition, make allowances when using the hot brush.
- Wait until the hot brush has cooled before putting it away into a bag or cupboard.

Tongs

Tongs, otherwise known as curling irons, are used to curl hair and differ from hot brushes because there is a smooth surface on the curling rod. The example shown in Figure 2.4 has a built-in stand which can be used for resting the tongs when they are not being used. The black tip at the end of the metal rod is a safety tip which enables the stylist to hold the tongs for extra control.

Figure 2.4 Tongs shown resting on their own stand (Courtesy BaByliss Ltd)

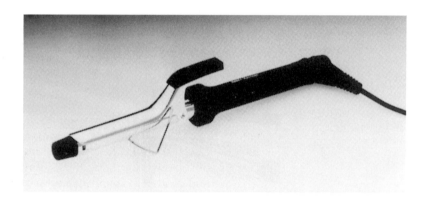

The flex has a swivel action to prevent the cord from tangling, allowing easier manipulation. The lever opens the tongs as it is depressed, then it is closed on the mesh of hair once the points are cleanly wrapped around the rod. The tongs are wound up the hair length and held in position until the heat has penetrated through the hair mesh. If curling right up to the roots, place a vulcanite comb between the tongs and the scalp to act as a barrier against the heat, as shown in Figure 2.5. Once the hair is released from the tongs, it should be allowed to cool before it is combed or brushed.

Figure 2.5 Protecting the scalp while using curling tongs: a heat-resistant comb is placed between the scalp and the tongs

Spiral tongs

Spiral tongs are curling irons which have a spiral groove running down the heated rod. Figure 2.6 shows a modern electric pair. This type of tongs has the same features as the ordinary tongs: built-in rest, protective safety tip and swivel flex. The lever is depressed and is closed on the hair points. As the tongs are turned, the mesh of hair will automatically position itself in the spiral groove running down the rod. Once the hair is sufficiently heated, the lever is opened, releasing a ringlet curl.

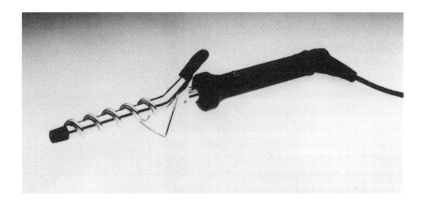

Figure 2.6 Electric spiral tongs shown resting on their own stand (Courtesy BaByliss Ltd)

Safe working guide – tongs

- Do not leave the tongs switched on for longer than necessary as this will shorten the life of the appliance and increases the chance of accidents.
- Use the built-in stand to prevent the scorching of work surfaces.
- Clean the appliance regularly, while disconnected from the mains. Use cotton wool and methylated spirit to remove dirt and never immerse in water.
- Use less heat on damaged hair and be especially careful on white or bleached hair as it can noticeably discolour if subjected to excessive heat.
- Wait until the tongs are cool before putting into a bag or cupboard.

New wave tongs

These tongs consist of three styling rods and a movable plate as shown in Figure 2.7, the third styling rod being under the plate. They are designed for creating deep, natural-looking waves. This type of tongs has similar features to those already described, as they have a built-in rest and swivel flex. As the handle is depressed the rods are closed against the grooves of the plate. If a slightly 'harder' effect is desired, rather like that from a marcel waving iron, remove the plate. The same safe working guide applies as for tongs.

Crimpers

Crimpers create straight line crimps in the hair in a uniform pattern. They can be used on all of the hair or in specific areas only, to produce a variety

Figure 2.7 The BaByliss New Wave can be used to create deep, natural-looking waves (Courtesy BaByliss Ltd)

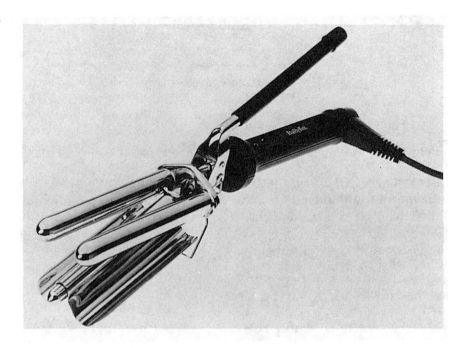

of effects. Crimpers, such as those shown in Figure 2.8, can be used to produce an interesting texture for straight hair, They can increase its volume, making it appear thicker.

A mesh of hair is taken about 2 cm (1 inch) deep and no wider than the metal plates of the crimper. They are then carefully positioned so that the plates are on both sides of the hair mesh where the crimp effect is desired. The crimpers are closed and held in position for 2–5 seconds, depending on the quality of hair, and then released. This procedure can be carried out repeatedly down the length of the hair until all the hair is crimped. Crimping the underneath hair of bobs gives added fullness and support to lank hair.

Figure 2.8 A pair of crimpers (Courtesy BaByliss Ltd)

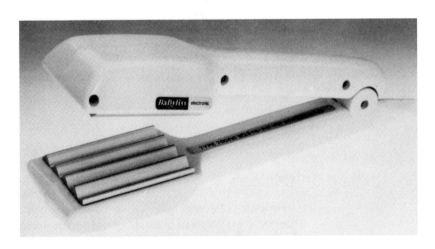

After crimping the hair, it can either be combed through, gently brushed, or left untouched for a less natural look. Brushing and combing crimped hair gives a softer look as the hard zig-zag lines which are produced by crimping become less apparent. (See safe working guidelines for tongs for additional information.)

Wave makers

Wave makers look and work like a crimper (see Figure 2.9) but instead of a tight crimping effect, they create deeper, softer waves. They can be used all over, or on certain areas only. The hair can be gently combed with a wide-toothed comb or the fingers afterwards, or alternatively, can be left to give deep firm waves.

Figure 2.9 An electric Wave Maker (Courtesy BaByliss Ltd)

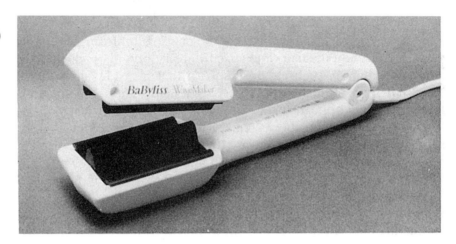

Straighteners

With most electrical hair appliances geared to curling or waving hair, it is refreshing to include straighteners. A modern electric straightener is illustrated in Figure 2.10. It works on the same principle as the crimpers but instead of creating crimps or waves, it irons out the curl or frizz. Electric straighteners are particularly useful for pressing super-curly hair to produce straighter looks. Please see safe working guidelines for additional information.

Electric clippers

Electric clippers have become increasingly popular in recent years for creating sharp and pronounced shapes on both European and Afro-Caribbean hair. They can be used to create strong outside shapes on the hairline only, or can be used to carry out a complete haircut.

Many types of electric clippers exist on the market, varying in weight, size and cutting precision. Rechargeable clippers are also available, meaning that they are totally portable, with an operating time of about 30 minutes before recharging is necessary. They are simply placed back into their special holding unit for recharging. The clippers shown in Figure 2.11 can have the blades adjusted so that an exact amount of hair is removed.

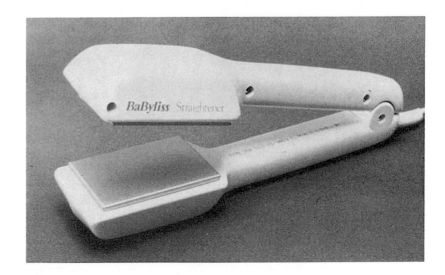

Figure 2.10 An electric pair of straightening irons, the Straightener (Courtesy BaByliss Ltd)

Figure 2.11 A pair of electric clippers (Courtesy Wahl Ltd)

Electric clippers work on the principle of one blade remaining fixed while the other moves across it. The action of the moving blade, operated by the motor, is similar to several pairs of scissors being used at the same time; as many as 14,400 cutting strokes can be made per minute with some types of clippers.

Basically, clippers are used by carefully placing in position and directing them as required. They are a particularly useful tool for creating etched lines in short styles and for cutting out partings in Afro hair.

It is important to keep your clipper blades well oiled with an oil specifically designed for that purpose. The blades should be aligned according to the manufacturer's instructions, so keep these when you purchase the clippers. If ever you draw blood, the blade should be removed and soaked in disinfectant, refitted, and finally re-oiled. Let us hope that one day a manufacturer will come up with some clippers which are easier to take apart and reassemble.

Heated rollers

Heated rollers are an asset for many clients because they achieve quick results and are relatively easy for an unskilled person to use. However, they can also be useful in the salon for a quick set or for adding curl and bounce. They are invaluable for session work when the stylist needs to be quick and the model is shared with the make-up artist.

Figure 2.12 shows a set of heated rollers. There are different sized rollers and each is positioned over a metal bar which heats it up. On top of each roller is a red dot which turns black when fully heated, indicating that the rollers are ready for use. The machine takes about ten minutes to heat up the rollers, so this time should be allowed for if you are using them. Once heated the rollers are taken off their individual heating elements as they are needed.

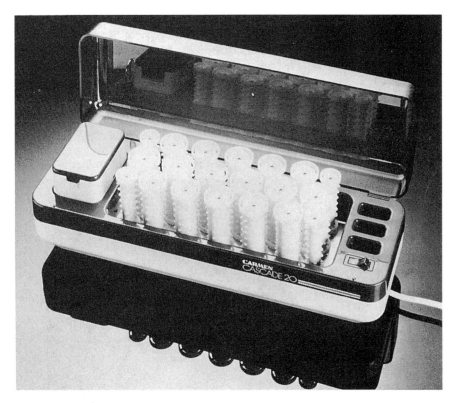

Figure 2.12 A set of heated rollers (Courtesy House of Carmen Ltd)

Heated rollers are put into the hair using the same method as for normal wet setting. However, equally good results can be achieved using slightly larger sections than normal (remember that the number of heated rollers that you have is limited).

If you look at the base of a heated roller you will find that it is colour-coded according to its diameter. Each size has its own colour-coded clip for securing the roller in position. The straight side of the clip should always be as near to the scalp as possible without causing discomfort. Using the wrong size of clip means that eventually the clips will become distorted.

When the rollering is complete, the rollers should be left in the hair until the indicator dot returns back to being red. For best results, leave until the rollers are completely cold. Remove the rollers by gently unwinding each roller (if you have wound up carefully and smoothly, the rollers will be easy to remove) and continue with styling.

Hood driers

Hood driers can be wall-mounted, fitted as a bank, or individually fitted on a pedestal with wheels. The need for hood driers has decreased as blow-drying has become more popular and many salons now save space by choosing wall-mounted driers.

Hood driers need to be dusted regularly and the upholstery of the seats should also be cleaned. If a build-up of fluff and dust is allowed to occur, it could shorten the life of the drier.

Figure 2.13 shows an example of a modern drier where the stylist is able to programme in the required drying time, and set the temperature. A warning 'bleep' indicates when the drying time is about to end.

Figure 2.13 A hood drier with its own built-in timer (Courtesy Wella Ltd)

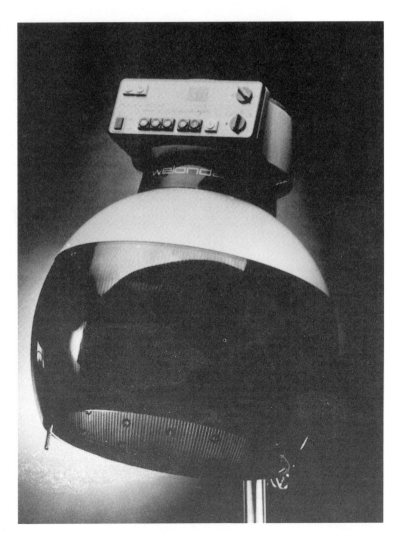

Pressing combs

Pressing combs are used to temporarily straighten Afro-type hair. Pressing combs used for thermal styling have teeth made from either stainless steel, brass or a combination of copper and brass and are available in different sizes. They are either heated directly by electricity and thermostatically controlled (like tongs and hot brushes) or, if they are like the one shown in Figure 2.14, are placed in a special heater until they reach the right temperature. The same safe working guidelines must be taken when using pressing combs as with other thermal styling equipment except that special agents are available to clean the teeth when there is a build up of carbon. After use, pressing combs should always be cleaned of hair and grease.

Figure 2.14 Pressing comb

Marcel waving irons

Marcel waving irons are old-fashioned curling irons which are still used today for theatrical wig styling. They are available in different sizes and are heated by placing in a special heater as shown in Figure 2.15. The larger of the two holes shown on the heater is used for heating while the smaller hole is for storing a spare set of irons while the others are being used. Rather than waste time waiting for the irons to heat, a person adept at using these irons would work with one set while the others are heating. As this type of curling iron is not thermostatically controlled, the user needs to test the temperature of the irons before placing them in the hair. This is normally done by closing them on a piece of white tissue. If the paper discolours, it indicates that the irons would scorch the hair. Marcel irons are held like other irons and opened by using the little finger to separate the handles as shown in Figure 2.16.

Figure 2.15 Marcel irons heater

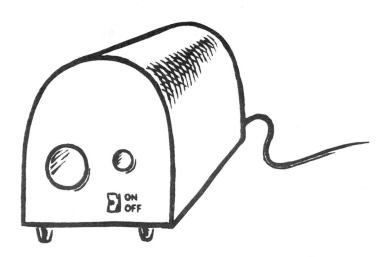

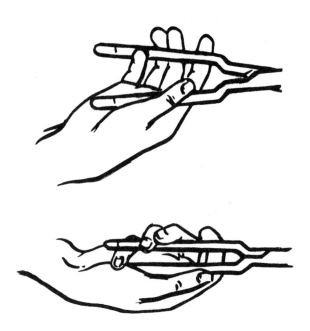

Figure 2.16 Holding and opening a pair of Marcel irons

Hairdressing tools

There is a proverb which says 'a bad workman always blames his tools'. In hairdressing, professional tools should be used to enable the operator to achieve the highest standards possible according to his or her ability. A comb or a pair of scissors bought from the local chemist will not withstand the frequent use encountered in a salon. This is why the major manufacturers produce tools to such high standards. Leave other tools for the non-professionals of the trade and equip yourself as well as you can afford.

Remember to look after your tools and they will give you years of service.

Clips

A number of different clips are used to hold the hair in place. They are best sterilised in disinfectants. The following are examples of clips.

Hair clamps

Figure 2.17 Plastic hair clamp

These types of clips are used to hold large quantities of hair when the hair needs to be sectioned for particular processes such as perming, cutting or colouring. They are made of plastic and come in a variety of different colours. The top of the clip is squeezed together to open the 'jaws' which end in short teeth. The jaws will close when the pressure is released from the top of the clip. Figure 2.17 illustrates a hair clamp.

Sectioning clips

Figure 2.18 Sectioning clip

These are usually made of metal and may be obtained with bright coloured coatings. The long prongs of the clip will hold quite large quantities of hair cleanly out of the way for the stylist. The end of the clip is squeezed together to open the prongs and close once the pressure is released. A sectioning clip is illustrated in Figure 2.18.

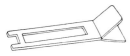

Figure 2.19 Double-prong clip

Double-prong clips

These are usually made of metal but plastic ones are also available. This type of clip is smaller than the others previously mentioned and they are not intended to hold large quantities of hair. They are used mainly to secure pincurls (see Chapter 5). Figure 2.19 illustrates a double-prong clip.

Hairpins and grips

As with hair clips, a number of different types is available for securing rollers or hair in place. They are best sterilised using disinfectants. The following are examples of pins and grips.

Figure 2.20 Fine wavy pin

Fine wavy pins

These pins are made of metal and are available in several shades to match different hair colours. They can be used to hold hair in place in the final dressing because they are fine, and if the right colour is used, can be effectively concealed in the hair. Fine wavy pins can also be used to secure flat pincurls in position and are preferred by many stylists for this because they do not mark the hair as much as metal double-prong clips. Because they are fine, the prongs are very pliable, with a tendency to bend, so are not effective for holding large quantities of hair securely. A fine wavy pin is illustrated in Figure 2.20.

Figure 2.21 Straight prong pin

Straight prong pins

Straight prong pins, otherwise known as setting pins, come in various colours to match the hair. They are also available in different lengths, the most common being 6–7 cm (3 inches) long. Apart from being used to hold rollers in place, they can also be effective for holding hair securely in place when dressing the hair. In the latter case, they would normally be used in conjunction with fine wavy pins. A straight prong pin is illustrated in Figure 2.21.

Figure 2.22 Plastic setting pin

Plastic setting pins

These are often preferred by stylists to the metal pins just described for securing rollers in place. They do, however, have a tendency to distort if they are misused by forcing them into rollers. A plastic setting pin is illustrated in Figure 2.22.

Figure 2.23 Hairgrip

Hairgrips

These are made of metal and come in a variety of colours. In North America they are called 'Bobbi' pins. They are available in both a shiny and matt finish, the latter being preferred for film and TV work, because they do not glint in bright light. The flat prong is always placed against the scalp as the wavy prong could cause discomfort. The two ends of the prongs are guarded by a plastic covering which resembles a small blob, protecting the client from the otherwise sharp ends. The blobs also make the opening of the grip easier. A hairgrip is illustrated in Figure 2.23.

Rollers

Rollers are made of plastic or metal, or a combination of both. They can be either cylindrical or conical and come in various lengths and diameters. Two are illustrated in Figure 2.24.

Figure 2.24 Cylindrical and conical rollers

The best types of rollers to use are smooth, because they do not mark the hair when it is wrapped around it. Spiked rollers may be easier to put in (because the hair will grip onto it), but they will mark the hair, especially if it is fine or fragile. Some stylists use a layer of tissue around spiked rollers when setting bleached hair to prevent marking or damage to the hair meshes. Another advantage of using smooth rollers is that they will never tangle in the hair.

There are rollers available which have a circular brush in their centre. They are made of metal wire loop and have a fine mesh covering, through which the bristles protrude. Again, although this helps to grip the hair there is evidence that damage is caused. In the United States it has been shown that these types of rollers can puncture the hair and damage it as it dries.

All rollers have perforations which allow the hair mesh to dry more quickly. Either metal or plastic pins can be used to secure the rollers in place (clips are more popular in the United States) but care should always be taken that the hair wrapped around the roller is not disturbed when it is secured. Rollers are best sterilised in disinfectant or a formaldehyde cabinet. They should be washed frequently.

Figure 2.25 Spiral curler

Spiral curlers

Spiral curlers are made of plastic and can be used for either setting or perming hair. They come in various lengths and diameters. One is illustrated in Figure 2.25. The hair is wrapped around the curler and sits in the spiral groove that runs down the entire length of the curler. Special plastic clips are used to fasten the points onto the curler. The result, whether set or permed, will be a ringlet curl.

Rik-Raks

Rik-Raks are made of plastic which is of a flexible 'V' shape, as shown in Figure 2.26. A mesh of hair is taken and woven through the two prongs in a figure of eight. The result is a deep wave in a zig-zag pattern. Rik-Raks can be used for setting or perming the hair.

Figure 2.26 A Rik-Rak

Molton Browners

The term 'Molton Browners' is now used to refer to many different types of 'rollers' that are available on the market. The original Molton Browners were created by the salon of the same name in London. They were soft, flexible rollers which consisted of a metal wire covered with padding and cloth. The central wire enables the roller to be bent to secure it in position. The hair should be dry for the cloth type of Molton Browner, so they can be used only for setting the hair.

Another type of Molton Browners is made of foam and can be used for both setting and perming hair because they do not absorb moisture from the hair so readily. (Wella market the foam type under the name of Molton Permers.) These also have a central spine of wire which enables them to be bent to stay in place. Figure 2.27 shows both types of Molton Browners, and there are many cheaper copies on the market.

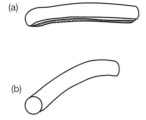

Figure 2.27 Molton Browners (a) original cloth-covered (b) foam

Mad Mats

Mad Mats resemble flat rectangles of J-Cloth which have sponge and wires running through them. They were developed by the Mad Hackers salon in London by Maureen and Kevin Bura. (Mad Mats are also featured in *Perming and Straightening – A Salon Handbook*.) They are reusable and are available in three widths and lengths. They can equally well be used for setting or perming. The hair can be curled, twisted, and even corrugated because Mad Mats can be easily manipulated into any shape. If long hair is being styled, extra Mats can be added. They do not require pins as they can just be bent over to secure the hair in place. A mesh of hair is simply placed on the Mat and it is then folded over.

Water sprays

Figure 2.28 Water spray

Water sprays are essential implements in every hairdresser's tool kit (see Figure 2.28). The bottle is filled with water and when the trigger is squeezed a sprayed jet or mist of water comes out of the nozzle. By adjusting the nozzle it is possible to adjust the fineness of the spray. Check the spray against your hand to check that it is correctly adjusted. Clients will not appreciate a strong jet of cold water being sprayed on their head! Change the water daily, and avoid leaving the bottle in direct sunlight. It can be very off-putting to see green algae in bottles which have been left in the sun, and it hardly makes a hairdresser look hygienic. A water spray should contain only water unless it has been labelled differently. It is a must for damping and redamping the hair.

Brushes

An extensive range of brushes is available for the hairdresser to choose from. Some of the brushes mentioned are for specific tasks or styling techniques, while others are more versatile and are used more frequently.

Basically, all brushes are made of bristles, which can be natural hog bristle, nylon or wire. These bristles are embedded into a wooden, plastic or rubber moulded handle. Natural bristles, although more expensive, are best for a brush, because they are made of natural keratin and there is less friction and wear on the hair in use. Natural bristle will also enable the hair to be penetrated, gripped and placed more easily. Nylon bristles are often criticised because of their hardness, as this will wear down the hair more, but the ends of the bristles can be rounded to avoid scratching the scalp and nylon can easily be cleaned and sterilised. Remember that the client will not be visiting the salon so often that your brush will cause excessive damage. The bristles of a brush must be set into tufts or rows, as this allows the loose or shed hair to collect in the grooves without interfering with the action of the bristles.

What effect has brushing on the hair?

Brushing transfers sebum from the skin along the cuticle of the hair shaft. This coating of oil helps to keep the moisture content of the hair constant at about 10 per cent. The oil reduces the tendency of the hairs to mesh together and tangle or form knots and the right amount of sebum will impart a natural lustre to the hair. It will also stimulate the circulation of the blood and lymph supplies to the scalp, removing waste products more efficiently and promoting hair growth. Brushing also helps remove dead skin cells and debris from the hair, which in turn will discourage the growth of micro-organisms such as bacteria and fungi.

If the sebaceous glands of a client are over-active, brushing will not tend to make the sebaceous glands noticeably more over-active. Brushing should still be carried out, but the hair should be shampooed more regularly. Brushing the hair will help to relax the client as well. The only really detrimental effect is that the hair will tend to become slightly damaged towards the front of the hairline, the cuticle becoming more roughened and the hair therefore becoming more porous.

How should hairbrushes be sterilised?

Before using a brush on a client it should be cleaned of all loose debris such as hairs and thoroughly washed. It should then be sterilised by placing it in a container of disinfectant for ten minutes, or as directed by the manufacturer. Remember that brushes can scratch the skin or take the top off spots, so they do need to be thoroughly sterilised. A formaldehyde cabinet can be used as an alternative, and brushes can be stored before use in an ultra-violet cabinet.

Flat brushes

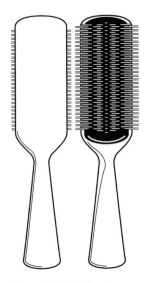

Figure 2.29 Flat brush

These brushes are probably the most commonly used in salons today (see Figure 2.29). A flat brush can be used for brushing the hair into shape after setting and also for blow-drying. It consists of nylon filaments embedded in a rubber base. The rubber base slides into position on the plastic moulded handle. The rubber base can be removed for cleaning and replacement tufts are available to replace ones which have become worn or damaged.

Vent brushes

These have open spaces along the back which allows the airflow from a drier to pass through – hence the alternative name of 'airflow brush'. The nylon tuft filaments are arranged in pairs, a shorter and longer one being embedded into the brush together. As the brush is drawn through the hair, the short and long filaments give the hair a broken, casual texture. If the particular hair being blow-dried has a slight natural movement, this will be increased when using a vent brush, because the airflow through the brush increases the hair's natural tendency to curl.

Vent brushes are also useful during a haircut, as the hair will fall into position allowing the stylist to identify any corrections to the cut that need to be made. A vent brush is shown in Figure 2.30.

Circular brushes

These come in different diameters varying from 1 cm to 6 cm. The tufts can be bristle, nylon or a mixture of both. Circular brushes tend to be used only when blow-drying. The diameter of the brush will determine how much volume and movement are put into the hair. A small diameter brush will put more curl into the hair than a larger one, in exactly the same way as this principle applies to roller sizes.

Figure 2.30 Vent brush

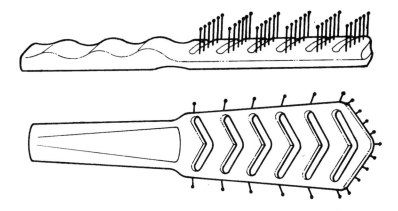

Circular brushes are shown in Figure 2.31.

Figure 2.31 Types of
circular brushes (Courtesy
Denman Ltd)

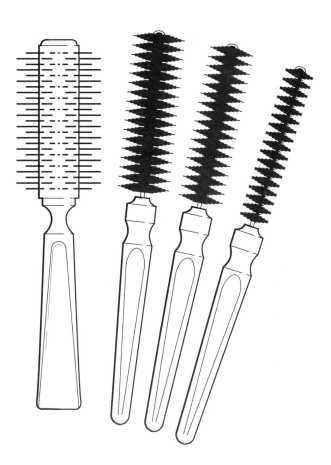

Figure 2.32 Neck brush

Neck brushes

The neck brush is used to clean hair clippings away from the face and neck. It is important that the bristles are long and soft, so that they do not cause discomfort to the client. Putting a little talcum powder on the brush will make wet hair clippings easier to remove from the skin. Use a neck brush repeatedly during a haircut to ensure client comfort. One is illustrated in Figure 2.32.

Tint brushes

This is a flat brush with a long narrow handle. The pointed end of the brush can be used to part the hair into sections when colouring the hair. The most expensive tint brushes have softer and closer tufts than the cheaper ones, helping to hold the product on the brush and being kinder to the client's scalp (they are less likely to scratch the scalp). Tint brushes can also be used to apply conditioner. One is illustrated in Figure 2.33.

Figure 2.33 Tint brush

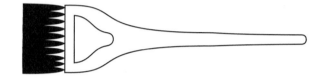

Combs

Hairdressing combs are made from nylon, plastic, vulcanite (a toughened, hard form of rubber) or metal. Metal combs are restricted in salons because of the damaging effects they can have on the hair and scalp but it is handy to have one as it can help remove static electricity from the hair. Because vulcanite combs are resistant to heat they are ideal when blow waving or tonging the hair. Some newer types of plastic are also extremely resistant to heat.

When purchasing combs, run your finger along the edge of the teeth, to see if they would scratch the scalp. The teeth of a good comb should have rounded points, with a fine taper and space between them where they join at the base. Avoid combs that pinch the hair at the base of the teeth, as these will tend to pull and tug the hair. Discard any combs which have damaged or missing teeth.

Combs should be regularly cleaned with hot soapy water and sterilised in disinfectant between clients. If you drop combs (or other tools) they should be sterilised before further use on a client: wiping them on a towel will not remove bacteria.

Damage to the hair may follow the incorrect combing of snarled up or knotted hair. Knots must be separated without undue effort or tugging on the shaft or scalp. Combing should commence at the ends and progress back towards the scalp.

Uses of combing

Combing will remove dead skin scales and debris from the scalp and hair. It also separates the hair into parallel strands which can be gathered into meshes of the required size. Combing can also remove excess water from

Figure 2.34 Tail combs

Figure 2.35 Straight comb

Figure 2.36 Large-toothed comb

Figure 2.37 Afro comb

the hair after it has been shampooed or rinsed. Tints and varlous creams can be distributed along the hair shaft by the comb, so that the application is evenly applied. A comb is invaluable for parting hair in a preliminary examination of the scalp to check for possible scalp conditions.

Tail combs

There are two types of tail combs from which a stylist can choose. One has a plastic 'tail' while the other has one made of metal. The metal-ended comb has a much finer end and is particularly useful when dividing the hair into fine sections, such as for perming or weave colouring. It is usually referred to as a 'needle' or 'pin-tail' comb, although in the United States it is referred to as a 'rat-tail' comb. Tail combs usually have only one size of teeth and are used primarily for sectioning the hair, as in setting, perming and weaving. The two types are illustrated in Figure 2.34.

Straight combs

These usually have two sizes of teeth and have no tail for making sections. Straight combs come in various sizes, the larger ones being used for disentangling and combing through tints. The more widely spaced teeth prevent pulling on the hair.

They are also used when cutting or dressing the hair after setting. Using a tail comb for this purpose has the disadvantage of having only one size of teeth. With a straight comb you can alternate between backcombing with the fine teeth and smoothing out with the larger teeth. Smaller teeth would drag out the backcombing when smoothing out the hair during dressing.

For certain cutting techniques, extra flexible straight combs are needed. An example is scissor over comb cutting, when a flexible thin comb is needed because it will bend according to the contours of the head, allowing the stylist to achieve a close cut. A straight comb is illustrated in Figure 2.35.

All-purpose combs

All-purpose combs have widely spaced teeth and a large handle. Because of the wide tooth spacing they are not used for styling, but are used for disentangling and combing products (such as tint and conditioners) through the hair. An all-purpose comb is illustrated in Figure 2.36.

Afro combs

These have long prong-like teeth made of metal or plastic set into a handle. The teeth are widely spaced because Afro hair is super-curly and ordinary combs would damage the hair. Many people with permed hair who dry it naturally find this type of comb invaluable. In use, the comb is inserted into the hair and used in a 'picking' action and this has led to the term 'hair pick'. Metal blades are more damaging to the hair; alternative materials are therefore preferable.

Because of the length of the teeth the Afro comb tends to be damaged more easily than some other combs. One is illustrated in Figure 2.37.

Haircutting tools

These can be divided into different types of scissors, clippers and razors. They are also the most likely to draw blood, and as such, are the most important implements to sterilise. Every time your tools draw blood they should be sterilised, and this can be achieved with a variety of disinfectants within about ten minutes without harming your precious tools. Be wary of placing your cutting tools into a formaldehyde cabinet as the vapours can attack and spoil metal. Instead, use ultra-violet cabinets as a handy storage area for your disinfected scissors. If you wish to work professionally, to the highest standards of hygiene, it is necessary to have two sets of cutting tools. Thus you always will have a spare while the other is being disinfected or has been sent off for sharpening. *The recommended method of sterilisation is with an autoclave (type of pressure cooker).*

Scissors

Scissors can be the most expensive non-electrical tools in the salon. Prices range from a few pounds to hundreds. As you will be using them for much of your working life you must have a pair that you use effortlessly, as if they were an extension of your hands. They vary in design, and intended use, and the following sections will take us through different scissor types. To work at their peak all scissors should be sharp.

If cutting tools are not sharp, they can damage the hair. This can clearly be seen from Figure 2.38. Good quality scissors will be made of well-tempered stainless or cobalt steel and have free-moving, sharp-edged blades. Scissors are available in different sizes ranging between 10 cm and 18 cm in length from the tip of the blades to the handles. The size a stylist chooses to work with depends on whichever type feels most comfortable and easy to control for the particular job being done. It is therefore usual to have more than one size in your kit so that you can alternate as the work you are doing changes.

(a) (b) (c)

Figure 2.38 Effects of cutting hair using blunt and sharp tools (Courtesy Wella Ltd) (a) a hair cut with blunt scissors (b) a hair cut with a blunt razor (c) a hair cut with a sharp razor

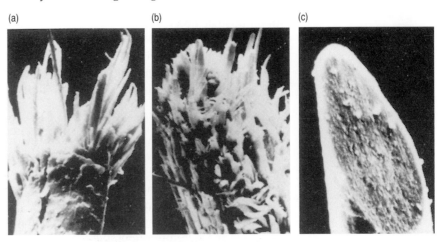

The various parts of a pair of scissors are shown in Figure 2.39 . Usually the points of the blades become blunt most quickly, because these are the parts which are used the most. The blade edges can either be micro-serrated or plain, some scissors having one type of each blade. The serrated edges tend to stop the hair from slipping during the closing of the blades when hair is being cut. The pivot of the scissors is usually a fixed screw which cannot be loosened or tightened, except when being sharpened professionally. Some manufacturers are now replacing this screw with more sophisticated arrangements which allow for adjustment to prevent premature slackening of the blades' action. The heel of the scissors is the part of the blades which is nearest the handles. The heel is used for taper cutting. The shanks can be made of either plastic or metal and vary in length. Handles can also be made of plastic or metal, and some have a cushion pad made of rubber or plastic between them to reduce noise when cutting.

Figure 2.39 The parts of a pair of scissors (a) points of blades (b) blade edges (can be plain or micro-serrated) (c) blades (d) heel (e) pivot (f) shanks (g) handles (h) cushion pads

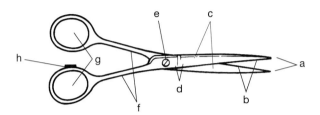

Caring for your scissors

- Wipe the scissor blades clean with a piece of cotton wool or tissue after each use to remove moisture and hair clippings, then sterilise them.
- Never cut anything other than hair with them or they will blunt more quickly.
- Never drop your scissors. It can upset their balance and performance. Carry them in their original protective case.
- Do not lend your scissors to others.
- If the blades do not move easily, try placing some high quality oil between the blades at the base of the handles.
- Always have them sharpened professionally – trade journals will carry advertisements for this.

Holding your scissors

All hairdressing scissors are held with the thumb and third finger as shown in Figure 2.40a This method of handling enables the operator to have maximum control over the scissors. When the scissors are not actually cutting, the thumb should be slipped out of the handle so that the scissors are cradled in the hand while still being supported by the third finger through the handle. By releasing the thumb from the handle the stylist has the manoeuvrability to hold a comb in the same hand, while ensuring that the scissor blades are not open. This is shown in Figure 2.40b.

Only the thumb moves when using scissors. Do not have the handle too far down on the thumb or it will restrict your freedom of movement. Spend time handling scissors before you attempt a haircut. Open and close them using only your thumb; one blade remains stationary while the other moves against it. Also, practise releasing and putting your thumb through the handle, holding a comb in the same hand as your scissors.

(a)

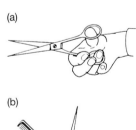

(b)

Figure 2.40(a) How to hold a pair of scissors (b) how to hold scissors and comb at the same time

Thinning scissors

There are two main types of thinning scissors: those which have both blades notched, and those which have one ordinary blade and one notched blade. Thinning scissors may also sometimes be described in the following terms:

- aescalups
- texturising scissors
- serrated scissors
- notched scissors.

Perhaps it is because thinning scissors have become popular again that the trade feels they should be referred to by more up-to-date names. Thinning scissors with two notched blades will remove less hair than a pair with one plain and one notched blade. The two types of thinning scissors are shown in Figure 2.41.

Figure 2.41(a) Thinning scissors with two notched blades (b) thinning scissors with one plain and one notched blade

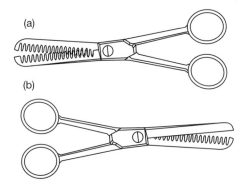

A word of warning: if you are doing a haircut and are alternating between conventional and thinning scissors, always check which ones you are holding before cutting hair with them.

Several new types of thinning scissors have been developed recently. The notched blades are now available with wider and narrower spaces between the teeth. These types of scissors are used to create various degrees of texture throughout a haircut. Some people argue that a good haircutter requires only one pair of conventional scissors to achieve the same results, but the advantage of the special scissors is that all-important commodity – time. It takes a long time pointing out or weave cutting hair, and this type of scissors makes the job a lot quicker.

Scissors with interchangeable blades are also available. Three different types are shown in Figure 2.42, while Figure 2.43 shows the result when used on the hair. These can achieve accurate results in one snip of the scissors.

Clippers

Electric clippers
These were described on p. 18.

Hand clippers
Hand clippers are not frequently used in the salon because of the greater popularity and extra safety of electric clippers. Their portability is also no

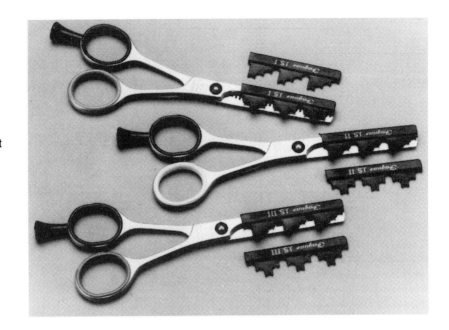

Figure 2.42 Scissors with interchangeable blades can be used to create a variety of different effects when cutting hair. These are the Jaguar Detour Stylers, showing JS I, II and III attachments. The scissors have a removable finger rest (Courtesy Rand Rocket Ltd)

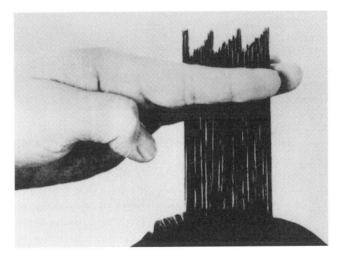

Figure 2.43 Point cutting of hair achieved in a single snip using the Jaguar Detour Stylers JS II (Courtesy Rand Rocket Ltd)

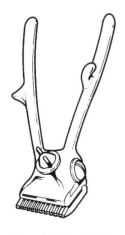

Figure 2.44 A pair of hand clippers

longer unique with the development of rechargeable electric clippers. Hand clippers are operated by squeezing the handles together, making the movable upper blade move across the fixed blade underneath. It is the distance between the points of the two blades and the spacing between the blade teeth that determine the closeness of the hair cut.

Clippers are available with different cutting heads, 0000 being the finest. If clippers pull on the hair, try cleaning and adjusting them. Never use clippers if any of the teeth are broken as the wider spacing between the teeth could result in dragging the hair and cutting the skin. A pair of hand clippers is illustrated in Figure 2.44.

Razors

The razors used in hairdressing have either a fixed blade that must be sharpened or a replaceable blade. Open or cut-throat razors can be either hollow-ground or solid-ground. A cut-throat razor is illustrated in Figure 2.45a.

The hollow-ground or German type is generally preferred by hairdressers for shaving. As the name implies, a hollow-ground razor has a hollow appearance between the edge and the back of the razor (see Figure 2.45b) and is made of a softer steel. A solid-ground or French razor has a different wedge-shaped blade and is the preferred razor for razor-cutting hair. The blade shape is shown in Figure 2.45c.

Figure 2.45(a) The parts of a cut-throat razor (b) cross-section of a hollow-ground blade (c) cross-section of a solid-ground blade

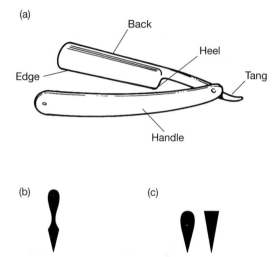

Hair shapers

Hair shapers are very similar to the cut-throat razor except that they have separated disposable blades. A hair shaper also has a metal guard which covers the cutting edge of the blade. Some hair shapers have a straight handle which is not used as a cover for the blade edge. The castellated guard-bar can be left on or taken off for shaping the hair. The hair shaper can also be used for shaving. The hair shaper illustrated in Figure 2.46 has its guard in place.

Figure 2.46 A hair shaper is similar to an open razor but uses a disposable blade which has a guard over it

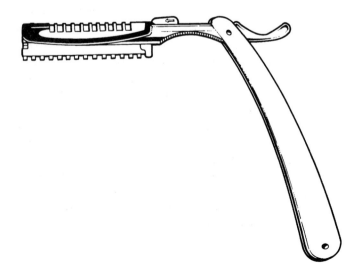

Care of razors

- Be careful never to drop your razor as this will damage the fine cutting edge.
- To prevent corrosion caused by moisture on the blade, strop the razor after use and apply a little fine oil.
- Care should be taken when opening or closing an open razor. Keep one hand at the base of the handle and the other on the shoulder of the razor. This way the fingers are kept away from the razor edge.
- Hold the open razor with the thumb on the underside of the shank and the little finger resting on top of the tang The other fingers should rest on top of the shank, as shown in Figure 2.47. You should be able to hold the razor firmly with this particular grip, so that it can move freely in all directions.
- Razors will require setting to maintain them. This involves the processes of honing and stropping. Honing is carried out to remove damage to the blade edge or to sharpen blades which have become exceptionally blunt. The stropping then maintains the sharpness of the blade.

Figure 2.47 How to hold a razor

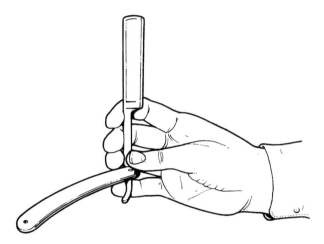

Honing

Two types of hones are available – natural or synthetic. Natural hones include slate, water and Belgian oilstones; these have a fine texture and a smooth surface. Synthetic hones include the carborundum stone and Indian hone; these have a coarse texture and a rougher surface. You can check for damage to the edge of a blade by running it gently against the edge of your thumb nail, a damaged blade will run unevenly against your nail.

If a blade is damaged it will require honing on a synthetic stone first to remove the damage quickly, followed by honing on a natural hone to get a fine edge to the blade (this is rather like rubbing down paintwork with coarse sandpaper to remove the paint, followed by fine sandpaper to prepare the surface for painting). Before honing commences, the surface of the hone should be lubricated with some water, spirit or oil, depending on its type. Then place the hone on a solid surface of a suitable height. The method of honing varies according to whether you are setting a hollow- or solid-ground blade.

Honing hollow-ground razors

Place the blade flat against the hone. Exerting equal pressure with each stroke, move the blade over the hone surface in a figure of eight. To turn the razor over at the end of this movement, so that the other side of the blade can be honed, turn the *razor* over and *not* your wrist. This will help ensure that equal pressure is exerted. Give both sides of the blade an equal number of strokes, decreasing the pressure with the last few strokes (see Figure 2.48 for how to hone a hollow-ground razor). Finish off the honing with a couple of single strokes each way.

Test the blade for sharpness by *gently* drawing the side of the blade edge across the moistened ball of your thumb, it should 'bite' or 'grip' the skin if it has a keen edge. This is due to the tiny 'saw teeth' that you have imparted to the blade edge during honing. They will eventually help grip the hair while cutting or shaving. A blade which is not sharp will run smoothly against the skin.

Figure 2.48 Honing a hollow-ground razor

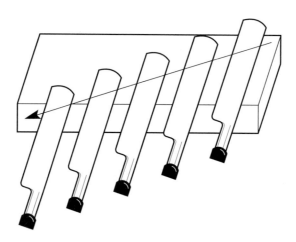

Honing solid-ground razors

Because a solid-ground or French razor is made of a softer steel, less pressure needs to be used when honing. The blade of the razor is placed flat on one end of the hone, with its blade edge pointing towards the centre of the hone. It is then slid, exerting little pressure, *across* and *along* the hone. The blade is then turned over, and the same procedure is carried out from the other end of the hone. You will be producing movements that make a 'V' towards the centre of the hone, as illustrated in Figure 2.49. Less strokes will be required to produce a keen edge. The strokes should eventually be made starting more towards the centre of the hone so that a smaller V is produced. The blade can be held slightly upright as honing finishes. Check against the moistened ball of the thumb for sharpness.

Stropping

Hollow-ground razors require a hanging strop which has one side made of canvas and the other side made of leather. Dry soap is used as a dressing for the canvas side and it is rubbed in using the side of a glass bottle. The leather side is gently scraped with a blunt knife to remove any old dressing and then either oil or tallow is rubbed in with the side of a glass bottle.

Figure 2.49 Honing a solid razor

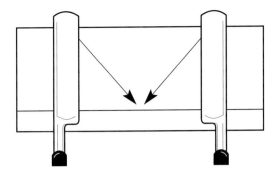

The strop used for solid-ground or French razors is called a hand strop. It consists of a piece of wood with a handle; this has leather on one side and balsa wood on the other. The dressing used on the leather and balsa wood is called 'Hamon paste', and this has a gentle abrasive action. There are two grades of Hamon paste, the finer one being used on the leather. The paste is used sparingly to avoid a build-up on the surface of the leather or balsa wood.

Stropping hollow-ground razors

The strop, secured to the wall at one end, is held outright by one hand so that it is taut. The blade is cleaned on the canvas side of the strop. The blade is then placed flat against the leather at the top of the strop, with the edge of the razor facing *away* from the centre of the strop. The blade is then gently drawn down the strop, turned over, and pushed up the opposite way. This is illustrated in Figure 2.50. After several strokes the razor should now be extremely sharp. This can be tested by taking a single hair between the fingers and cutting it with the razor. If it is sharp, the blade will cut the hair without 'pushing' it.

Stropping solid-ground razors

The strop is placed on a level surface and a few strokes are made on the balsa wood, as described below, to align the teeth that have been formed when honing. The balsa wood is used first because it is covered with the more abrasive Hamon paste. The hand strop is now turned with the leather side up. The blade of the razor is placed against the leather side of the strop so that the edge is facing away from the centre of the strop. The blade is then pushed along and across the strop in an inverted 'V' movement. The blade is then turned and the movement is repeated in the opposite direction. These movements are illustrated in Figure 2.51.

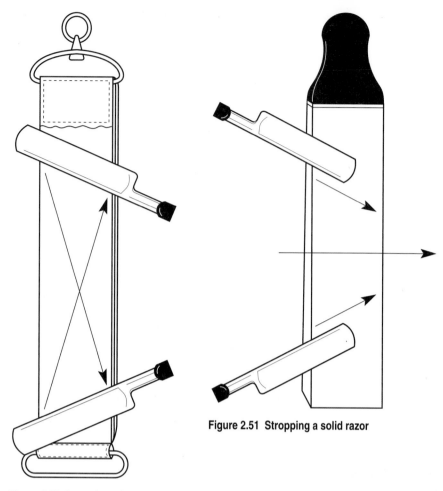

Figure 2.51 Stropping a solid razor

Figure 2.50 Stropping a hollow-ground razor

1 Which regulations impose duties upon the employer about equipment used in the workplace?

2 What is the purpose of the filter on a hand-held hairdrier?

3 List some safety precautions to be taken when using a hand-held drier.

4 How can the concentration and direction of the airflow of a hand-held drier be changed?

5 When using a hot brush, how are buckled ends avoided?

6 What is an 'independent' hot brush?

7 How is the scalp protected from heat when using tongs?

8 List the main safe working guidelines to be followed when working with thermal styling equipment.

9 How do electric clippers operate to cut hair?

10 On what type of hair would you use a pressing comb?

11 Give an example of when you would use the following:

(i) flat brush

(ii) vent brush

(iii) circular brush

(iv) tail comb

(v) straight comb

(vi) Afro comb

12 How and when would you sterilise cutting tools?

13 Why should hair cutting scissors be kept sharp?

14 How are a pair of scissors held?

15 What are thinning scissors used for?

16 What is the difference between the blades of a hollow-ground and solid-ground razor?

17 How does a hair shaper differ from an open blade razor?

18 How would you check a razor's blade for damage and sharpness?

19 What is the purpose of honing?

20 What is the purpose of stropping?

Advanced Questions

1 Devise notes and diagrams to show correct handling and use of a range of electrical equipment.

2 Draw and label the parts of a pair of scissors.

3 Explain how hair cutting scissors should be cared for and maintained.

4 Describe different types of razors, their uses and how they are cared for.

5 Make an outline of what you would include for a new junior's induction to the various pieces of equipment in the salon.

Chapter 3

DESIGN ANALYSIS

Identifying clients' requirements by consultation

Consultation, as defined by dictionaries, will refer to 'a meeting of two or more persons to deliberate and discuss a matter which requires specialist expert knowledge'. In the salon, the hairdresser is the consultant because he or she possesses the expert technical knowledge. The client is given a consultation which will either be to ask the opinion of, or take the advice of the expert.

The terms consultant and consultation are strongly linked to professions that revolve around the process of consultation: the solicitor, doctor, dentist, etc. When we visit dentists they tell us what should be done to our teeth; they do not ask us how many fillings we would like or whether we want an extraction. However, in many salons it is quite a different story. Some hairdressers *ask* their clients what size of roller they want in their hair: that is certainly neither a professional approach nor a consultation.

A consultation is a *process* which means it requires active participation from all the parties concerned for it to be successful. Although this will be usually just you and the client, it could also involve a parent in the case of a younger client. It is not a matter of a hairdresser telling the client what is needed, which is a one-way line of communication. Consultation should be involved with making suggestions, offering expert advice and seeking approval from the client to perform a service at an agreed price. This process obviously takes time and allowances to carry it out properly need to be made in the way the salon arranges appointments. Time spent with the client *before* the service is begun is as important as the time the hairdresser actually spends working on the client's hair. Without the consultation, the hairdresser is reduced to being a menial performing a technical skill as opposed to a professional responding to the needs and requirements of individual clients.

This process can be described as a flow chart:

The consultation process

Client enters salon
↓
Client is greeted and offered a seat
↓
Client is given a consultation by the hairdresser
↓
Agreement is made (by client and hairdresser) on course of action
↓
Service is given or postponed to future date

Finding out exactly what you need to do to clients' hair to make them satisfied can be a lengthy and difficult process. Please notice that there is no reference to 'what the clients want', because in many cases they do not know and have gone to the hairdressers to be offered advice about what will suit them and their hair type.

All consultations should be carried out before a service begins and when the hair is still dry. You should have checked the condition of the hair and scalp for any signs of disease or damage. During the consultation, you will need to ask plenty of open-ended questions to elicit all the necessary information that will assist you and your client in selecting the most appropriate options from those which are available. Please remember that clients may not always be totally honest with the answers they give you because they may fear retribution or that a service might not be given if they tell the truth.

Choosing a hairstyle

Sometimes, clients may have a very clear idea of how they want their hair to look, and often bring pictures with them, cut out of magazines. A particular actress or singer may have a hairstyle that they admire, and they may ask you to make their hair look the same. (Do not make the mistake of pretending you know the actress or singer they are talking about if you haven't got a clue who they are, let alone what their hair looks like.) Clients will often choose a look that, in your professional opinion, is totally unsuitable for them. Unsuitable styles are sometimes chosen by clients because they want to be like the image of the model in the picture. The picture will probably be showing an attractive, youthful person with glowing skin, perfect teeth and an abundance of healthy, shining hair. You look at the client who has handed you the picture and your heart sinks. *Never*, however, make derogatory remarks about a client's request or laugh at any suggestions. Saying things like 'I know I'm good but I can't perform miracles' or 'You can't make a silk purse out of a sow's ear' should be said only in the privacy of the staff room, if they must be said at all. In such an instance, you will need to make alternative suggestions to your client, perhaps based on their original idea, or a new option all together. Always try to say something positive about their unsuitable suggestions so that you respond in a pleasant way while at the same time putting your expert advice across.

For example:

- To client with protruding ears who chooses a style that will emphasise them:
    'The back would look great like that, but if we leave it a little longer at the sides, it will lie a lot better over the ears. What do you think of that idea?'
- To client with a high forehead who wants her hair swept straight back from her face:
    'How do you feel about having a fringe? If we sweep it across like this, it will add softness to the style and will emphasise your nice cheek-bones.'
- To client with out of condition hair who wants a perm, which you know will be a disaster:

'If you have a series of remoisturising treatments, your hair will be in better condition and the perm result will be far better. How do you feel about having your perm in a few weeks' time when your hair is back in condition? You could have the first of the remoisturising treatments today.'

Can you see how, in these examples, the hairdresser puts across suggestions without saying anything derogatory, but at the same time seeks confirmation from the client about the action to be taken?

Many hairdressers find it useful to use visual aids to assist them in discussing ideas and specific looks with clients. Visual aids include style books, photographs around the salon, the hair of colleagues, shade charts, and so on.

Face shape in relation to hair design

Whatever the cutting or styling technique used, the one factor that never changes is the importance of creating a style to suit the shape of the face. We can isolate facial form into the seven principal shapes, illustrated in Figure 3.1:

- oval
- oblong
- square
- triangular
- inverted triangular (heart)
- diamond
- round

The oval face is considered as the ideal shape for which to design a hairstyle. This is because there are no irregular contours or proportions present which will need to be balanced or camouflaged by the hair design. Therefore, it can be said, that when dealing with all of the other face shapes, we are aiming at creating the *illusion* of an oval face by the line and balance of the hairstyle.

When we create the illusion of something being different from what it is, we are controlling the way in which it is to be perceived by others. This concept is demonstrated in Figure 3.2 which shows how the arrangement of lines and shapes alter our perception of what we are seeing. As hairdressers, we create similar illusions by using the hair to alter the appearance of a person's face and head shape by the way the hair is used to frame it.

The principle of balancing facial shape can be seen in the series of diagrams in Figure 3.3.

Table 3.1 describes the styles that can be used under two headings: positive styles (styles that work to make the face shape appear oval) and negative styles (styles that should be avoided as they do nothing towards making the face appear oval or emphasise bad features).

Figure 3.1 The seven principal shapes of facial form

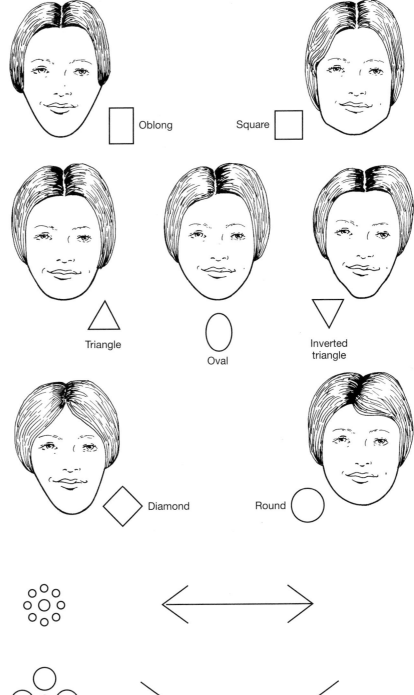

Oblong

Square

Triangle

Oval

Inverted triangle

Diamond

Round

Figure 3.2 Perception in hair design (a) The centre circles are exactly the same size but they look different because of what has been placed around them (b) Both lines are exactly the same but one appears longer than the other because of the way the arrow lines are pointing

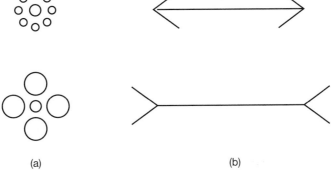

(a)

(b)

Figure 3.3 Balancing face shapes

Face shape   Correction

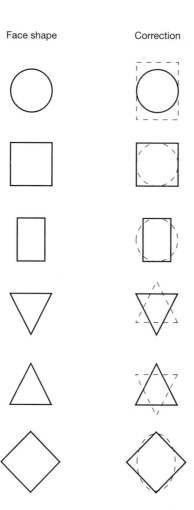

Table 3.1 Positive and negative hairstyles

Positive styles	Negative styles
Round Styles which add height and are long and narrow through the sides	Styles which accentuate the roundness of the face, such as tight perms, one-length cuts and round shapes
Square Round shapes which soften the angular lines of the face	Square cut bobs, geometric or angular shapes
Oblong Asymmetrical shapes which widen the face and add interest	Styles which are short at the sides and nape and are swept upwards to create height
Inverted triangle or heart Styles which are full at the bottom to widen the chin and narrow through the top	Styles which are high and wide through the cheek-bone area, as these emphasise the narrow chin
Triangular Shapes which are wide and full through the top and narrower through the sides; longer hair will detract from any angular jawline	Styles which are cut narrow through the top or very short styles, as these both emphasise the wide jawline
Diamond Round shapes which soften the angular lines of the face, which are narrow through the sides and mid-chin length to widen the chin	Styles which are high, short or full at the sides, as these emphasise the narrow chin and wide cheek-bones

Head shape

Although our heads all consist of the same bones and conform to a recognisable 'skull' shape, there will be differences of form in some clients to be noted by the stylist. Feel the client's head with your hands. Are there any protrusions? Notable differences in head shape can be felt in the parietal and occipital areas (see Figure 3.4). Some heads are either flatter or rounder here, and you may have to make adjustments in the style so the hair lies as you intend it to. You may also discover warts, cysts or scarring which were not evident from just combing the hair.

Figure 3.4 Main bones of the human skull

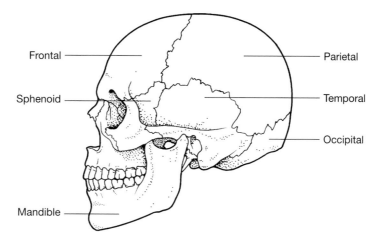

Frontal — Parietal
Sphenoid — Temporal
— Occipital
Mandible

Body shape

Just as there is an ideal face shape there is also an ideal in body proportions. The height of a person should be seven or eight times the size of their head. If someone is short the hairstyle should be designed to give an illusion of extra height, while the opposite would be true for someone who is tall. The hairstyle should balance and harmonise with the height and build of the client. If the head of the client looks small, design a style to make it look bigger; if it looks large, design one to make it look smaller. Remember to take a look at clients while they are walking to gauge their exact height and the way they 'carry' themselves. There are no 'hard and fast' set rules about designing a style to suit body shape as face shape and facial features are so important in coming to the correct conclusion.

Facial features

Facial features include the eyes, nose and mouth. Styles can be designed which detract from or emphasise such facial features. An example of this is when a large prominent nose may be detracted from by dressing the front hair slightly at an angle, rather than symmetrically. Straight fringes will draw attention to wrinkled eyes whereas they will be softened by dressing the hair angled away from the face. A prominent profile will be accentuated by a style swept backwards off the face, so it is better to have the hair softly framing the face.

The neck

A long 'swan' neck will be accentuated if the hair is cut short or unswept at the nape, so the hair should be kept long to disguise the neck. Similarly, a short neck will be lengthened by cutting the hair short in the nape.

The ears

Protruding ears can be disguised by dressing the hair over them. Often a person's ears are not evenly balanced so that one ear may appear to protrude more than the other or be positioned slightly lower. If there is a very obvious difference, you may need to leave the hair slightly longer on one side than the other to rectify the imbalance or to allow for more protrusion on one side.

Hair density

Density is the term that describes the amount of hairs on a person's head, or more exactly, how closely spaced the hairs are. The more hairs per square centimetre or inch, the denser the hair is. Because of hair density, it may not always be possible to recreate certain styles on individual clients. Hair density may also differ on different areas of the same head. Actually put your fingers into the hair of the client to assess the density. Words used to describe density include thick, medium, fine and sparse.

Hair texture

Hair texture refers to the thickness or diameter of individual hairs. It can be judged by taking individual hairs between the thumb and forefinger to feel whether they are fine, medium or thick. You will also be able to feel whether the hair is soft and pliable or coarse and hard. The term texture can also be used to describe how curly, wavy or straight the hair is and this should be considered for the suitability of particular hairstyles. For example, very curly hair would be difficult for the client to manage if it was cut into a square bob and stretched smooth by blow-drying, as it would quickly revert back to being curly. Words used to describe texture include wiry, coarse, fine, pliable, frizzy, wavy, straight, hard and lank.

Hair condition

The condition of the hair is important because the stylist should establish any previous chemical or physical damage that the hair has sustained. For example, highly bleached hair will have suffered from internal oxidation damage to the cortex, as well as external damage to the cuticle. It will be less elastic than hair in good condition and will therefore not hold a set or blow-dry as well. Hair condition can be assessed by carrying out porosity and elasticity tests. Words used to describe condition include dry, damaged, sensitised, split, oily, porous, dull and shiny.

Previous treatments

It is always important to establish the previous treatments that the client has had. You will need to question your clients about the number of chemical treatments that they have had done on their hair and how they usually care for their hair between salon visits. In effect, you need to build up a hair history for your clients. Examples of questions you may need to ask are set out below with reasons for asking them. These questions are not in any specific order and they may not all be relevant to every client situation:

- 'When did you last shampoo your hair?' (Helps to diagnose activity of sebaceous glands.)
- 'What shampoo do you use at home?' (Indicates what hair type the client thinks they have and their approach to home hair care.)
- 'When did you have this perm? What did you think of the result?' (Tells you what the client expects from a perm.)
- 'Have you ever had any form of colorant used on your hair?' (Tells you if the hair colour you are seeing is natural – avoid using words like dye or bleach.)
- 'Have you ever had any major colour change?' (Tells you whether the hair has been chemically treated when it is not showing obvious signs of this.)
- 'How long ago was your hair last cut?' (Indicates how much the hair has grown since it was cut.)
- 'Are you on any medication or have you recently had an operation?' (The general health of hair often deteriorates when a person is taking certain medication, is ill or has undergone anaesthesia.)

While you are asking these questions. it is a good idea to be seated next to your client in a position that encourages intimacy so that the client feels 'safe' to answer you honestly, or ask while examining the client's hair. *Never* look at a client's hair with disgust as you examine it. This is both embarrassing and unnecessary. Even if you think the last salon ruined the client's hair, there is no need to say it. Clients would not be sitting in front of you if they thought *that* salon had done a good job. It is unprofessional to criticise the work of another hairdresser and it makes clients feel uncomfortable when you do so. You should not be on an ego trip about your own standards. If a client ever asks you directly 'Do you think they ruined my hair?' a good way of answering is to say something like, 'Well, you obviously aren't happy with it and I think we can improve how it looks'. By responding in this way, you are not drawn into the trap of finding fault with another salon. You can never really be sure that the client went to that salon or if the damage was done by the client at home.

Hair growth patterns

The direction of hair growth is very important because nothing a stylist can do will alter how the hair grows naturally. This means that forcing the hair in the opposite direction to its growth can often spell disaster because it will not lie properly and will fight to lie in its natural direction. This is particularly evident if a widow's peak is present on the front hairline, for example.

A widow's peak is a strong, centre forward growing peak of hair found on the front hairline. Trying to style the hair into a full fringe would be difficult because it is going against the direction of the natural growth. The stylist may manage to make the hair look acceptable but the hair would soon separate and lift at the widow's peak and the client may find it very difficult to manage.

A cowlick is also found on the front hairline and is a strong growth of hair which grows in a sworl. Again, fighting the natural hair growth direction is not recommended. It is better to work with the natural lie of the hair.

The nape hairline will have its own unique pattern of growth. It may be low in the neck and grow to one side or be high and grow into the centre. The hair at the nape should not be forced against its natural growth or it may stick out the day after styling. It is not usually recommended to cut above the natural hairline because of this problem, but false hairlines can be created using scissors, razors or clippers.

The crown is usually situated at the top or back of the head and forms the natural hair growth pattern for this area. Occasionally two crowns may be detected, referred to as being a double crown.

A natural parting is where the hair falls and parts naturally from the front hairline to the crown(s).

The true lie of the hair can truly be seen only when the hair is wet because certain hair growth peculiarities may be disguised by the styling technique used previously by the client. The amount of lift at the roots of the hair can also more easily be seen when the hair is wet. Look for unusual root movements and hair growth direction. Words used to describe hair growth include cowlick, widow's peak, crown, natural parting, root lift, root direction and so on.

Figure 3.5 shows how different hair growth patterns are more suitable for particular styles than others.

The client

The client's lifestyle

Clients' lifestyles often determine the amount of time and money that they can afford to spend on their hair. A young, working mother may not be able to give a lot of time to her hair and so would want a style that is easily managed. Certain occupations such as nursing and the police place restrictions on individuals to conform to particular regulations for their hair. It may be that the hair must be worn up at work or that it should not touch the neck of a uniform.

The occasion

Although the majority of the stylist's work consists of everyday, wearable styles, clients often go to a salon for their hair to be styled for a special

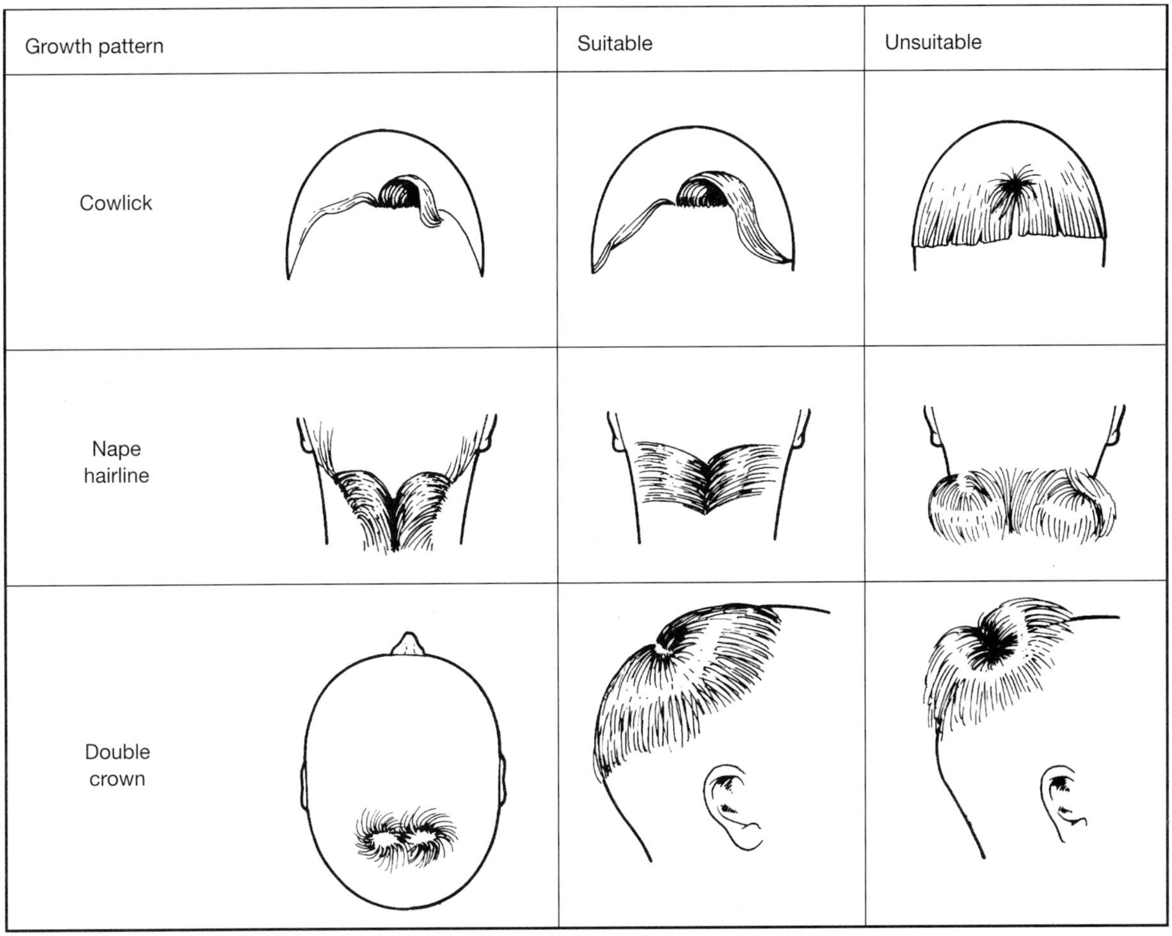

Growth pattern	Suitable	Unsuitable
Cowlick		
Nape hairline		
Double crown		

Figure 3.5 Suitable and unsuitable styling techniques for particular hair growth patterns

occasion. The best example is the bride who wants to have her hair different for her wedding day. In this instance, the stylist should see the client for several appointments before the 'big day' to work on different ideas which complement the head-dress, veil and outfit. Some salons have set up a bride service which offers special rates if all the bridesmaids and some guests visit the salon. A stylist may visit the family home immediately prior to the wedding to attend to the head-dresses, veils, hair and make-up.

The client's age

Ultimately it is the bone structure of the client's face and head that determine the most suitable style. Modern styles can and should be worn by the older client, the difference being that hard lines should be softened and movement should be added to the style, as this is more flattering than very straight lines. Judge the age of your client – do not ask!

Design analysis – at a glance

Until design analysis becomes second nature, so that you do it unconsciously, use the guidelines in Figure 3.6. Tick the appropriate boxes and enter any necessary details. You may find that the quality of the hair, things like texture and condition, falls in more than one category. Keep this list well away from the client!

Preparing the client

Gowning the client

A client's clothes must be adequately protected by a gown from both hair clippings and products. If a client's clothing is spoilt, they are within their rights to sue the salon. If hair clippings get inside clothing the client will be itching for hours afterwards, and not thinking very kindly of the salon.

Every client should have a freshly laundered gown. If this is not possible, no part of the gown should come into direct contact with the client's skin; a neck strip of disposable crêpe paper should be placed between the client's neck and the gown.

Gowns should be made of cotton or a mixture containing some cotton (polyester and cotton, etc.), as this will be more comfortable for the client to wear, especially in hot weather. Gowns can either be tied at the neck or be the wrap-over type with a tie belt at the waist. Whichever type is used, gowns should be large enough to cover the client's clothing adequately and should not be tied too tightly.

When should a plastic cape be put on a client?

Plastic capes are used in many salons when perming, colouring or cutting, as an added protection. They are put on over the gown and are secured at the neck. Always make sure that jewellery and clothing (such as high-necked sweaters) are not causing an obstruction. Politely ask your client to remove such items if they might be damaged, or if they could hinder you while working on the client. Be careful not to get the gown caught on a jewellery clasp; there are few sights as embarrassing as beads from a necklace falling about all over the floor.

Preparing the client's hair

Combing and brushing the hair before a service

The hair should be combed and then brushed during the initial discussion that takes place between the stylist and the client at the beginning of the appointment. However, the hair should be only combed and not brushed before a chemical treatment such as perming or tinting. This is because brushing could scratch and irritate the scalp.

FACE SHAPE

Oval ☐	Oblong ☐		
Square ☐	Triangular ☐		
Heart ☐	Diamond ☐		
Round ☐			

BODY SHAPE

Tall and lean ☐
Short and heavy ☐
The ideal ☐
Short upper body with slim waist ☐
Slim upper body with heavy thighs ☐

HEAD SHAPE

Scars ☐
Cysts ☐
Warts ☐
Details of protrusions in occipital and
parietal areas: _____

FACIAL FEATURES

Features to emphasise: _____

Features to disguise: _____
_____

THE NECK

Long and slim ☐
Short and heavy ☐
Long and broad ☐
Short and slim ☐
Average ☐

THE EARS

Degree of protrusion: _____

Average size ☐
Large ☐
Small ☐

HAIR DENSITY

Thick ☐
Average ☐
Thin ☐
Sparse ☐

HAIR TEXTURE

Coarse ☐	Wiry ☐
Frizzy ☐	Hard ☐
Pliable ☐	Soft ☐
Wavy ☐	Straight ☐
Curly ☐	Lank ☐
Fine ☐	Other ☐

HAIR CONDITION

Split ☐	Porous ☐
Sensitive ☐	Dull ☐
Dry ☐	Oily ☐
Shiny ☐	Breakage ☐

Details of previous chemical
treatments: _____
_____

HAIR GROWTH PATTERNS

Cowlick ☐
Widow's peak ☐
Double crown ☐
Natural parting ☐
Areas of recession: _____
Front hairline: _____
Nape hairline: _____
Side hairline: _____

CLIENT'S LIFESTYLE & OCCASION

Frequency of salon visits: _____
Details of limiting factors influencing
choice of style: _____

Everyday style: ☐
Details of special occasion: _____

AGE GROUP

Under 5 ☐	6 - 11 ☐
12 - 15 ☐	16 - 19 ☐
20 - 25 ☐	26 - 30 ☐
31 - 35 ☐	36 - 40 ☐
41 - 45 ☐	46 - 50 ☐
51 - 60 ☐	60+ ☐

Figure 3.6 Design analysis – at a glance

Why should the hair be combed and brushed before a service?

Combing and brushing the hair makes it easier to work with and more comfortable for the client. It frees the hair from tangles, previous back-combing, dust, dirt and scaling, and loosens hairspray. You can also check the scalp for lice and nits without the client being aware.

How should the hair be combed?

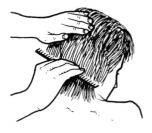

Figure 3.7 Disentangling hair, one hand supporting the head

Using a wide-toothed comb, begin in the nape region at the points of the hair, gradually working upwards towards the scalp. The hand not holding the comb should be positioned as shown in Figure 3.7, to support the head. The comb should be held upright, not flattened which would scratch the head, and drawn through the hair without pulling or tugging. As each mesh of hair is combed, another mesh of hair is taken and the same procedure is followed, working over the entire head. Hair should not be combed starting at the roots because the tangles will be pushed down to the points. If this happens the tangles are difficult to remove and will cause discomfort for the client.

Why should the hair be brushed?

Hair is brushed before a service for the following reasons:

- to relax and soothe the client
- to remove loose hair and debris
- to stimulate the blood supply to the scalp.

NB Wet hair should never be brushed to remove tangles as this causes over-stretching and subsequent breakage.

How should the hair be brushed?

After combing, the hair can be brushed using either single or double brushing, as illustrated in Figure 3.8.

Figure 3.8 Single and double brushing

Single brushing Using one hand to support the head, the hair is brushed beginning at the hair points at the nape, gradually brushing closer to the scalp. This is continued over the whole head in a smoothing, stroking action.

Double brushing As the name implies, double brushing is carried out using two hairbrushes. The brushes are used in a rolling action with one of the brushes always in contact with the hair. As one of the brushes leave the hair, the other hand rolls over the first in a smooth, consistent pattern of movement. This type of brushing usually precedes a hair treatment.

Making partings

There are no rules about making partings in hair; they can be any length, at any angle and at any place on the head. Partings can be straight, curved, slanted, zig-zag, high, low, centre or side. The purpose of a parting is to assist in creating an illusory effect in hair design, as shown in Figure 3.9.

Figure 3.9 Making partings (a) Straight partings from the forehead to the crown will add length to the face (b) Short partings increase the height of the head and the style (c) The greater the angle of the parting, the wider the head will appear

(a)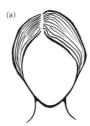
(b)
(c)

Finding the natural parting

A natural parting can be found only when the hair is wet. After disentangling, comb the hair back straight from the face using the wide teeth of your comb. Keep the hair combed close to the head and then place your other hand on the head and gently nudge the hair forward. The hair will then break to reveal the natural parting.

Although it is usually recommended to use the natural parting, it is sometimes necessary to make your own parting elsewhere. Working against the natural parting is useful for obtaining height in some styles and the clever placing of a parting can cause thin faces to appear broader and wide faces to look narrower. Many men with thinning heads of hair assume that having a low side parting will make them appear to have more hair. When making a parting, to balance the comb, place your index finger on top of the comb.

Revision Questions

1 Explain why it is important to carry out a consultation at the beginning of an appointment.

2 Name the seven principal face shapes.

3 Why is an oval face considered the ideal?

4 How can head shape influence design analysis?

5 What is the ideal body shape?

6 How could prominent ears be disguised?

7 What is hair density?

8 How could hair texture influence the selected style?

9 Why are hair growth patterns important considerations?

10 Name three different hair growth patterns.

11 How does the age of the client influence the selected style?

12 Why should a client wear a gown?

13 If the salon is unable to provide each client with a clean gown, what hygiene measure should be taken?

14 Why should the hair be combed and brushed before a service?

15 How should the hair be combed?

16 Give three reasons for brushing hair before a service.

17 Why should wet hair not be brushed?

18 What is double brushing?

Advanced Questions

1 Describe how you would influence a client's choice of hairstyle and what action you would take if the choice of style was unsuitable.

2 With the aid of diagrams, describe the corrective measures you would take for each of the following face shapes:

   (i) oblong

   (ii) square

   (iii) triangular

   (iv) inverted triangle (heart)

   (v) diamond

   (vi) round

3 Explain the importance of each of the following in design analysis:

   (i) head shape

   (ii) body shape

   (iii) facial features

   (iv) the neck

   (v) the ears

   (vi) density, texture and condition of the hair

   (vii) hair growth patterns

   (viii) client's lifestyle, age, and the occasion

4 With the aid of diagrams describe different hair growth patterns and how they influence the choice of hairstyle.

5 Devise your own design analysis checklist for use in the salon.

6 Collect a range of photographs from fashion or trade magazines and classify them according to face shape.

Chapter 4

CUTTING

Introduction

There is more to cutting hair than simply reducing its length. It takes technical skill, care and imagination to produce good results because every head presents its own problems. If you are following an SVQ/NVQ, there are a number of haircuts that you will be required to perform. This chapter looks at cutting in its wider context so that you can apply the knowledge to the various styles. You will find some photographs of step-by-steps later in the chapter.

A good haircut is the basis of a manageable style and is usually a high priority when clients choose a stylist or a salon. A competent hairdresser is equipped with *all* the cutting skills necessary to carry out a client's request and carefully selects the appropriate techniques to achieve the required effect.

Client consultation

The time you spend with your client before you start cutting is as important as the time you actually spend working with your scissors. Be absolutely sure that you and your client are clear and in full agreement of what you intend to do to the hair. This will mean showing the client how much you intend cutting off rather than explaining in measurements that can often be misinterpreted. It is surprising how one person's concept of half an inch (1.25 cm) can differ from another's!

Natural hair fall and movement

Every head of hair is unique and will present you with a different set of problems to solve and decisions to make in order to achieve a satisfactory result. The stylist should always work *with* the natural fall and movement of the hair so that the finished style lies correctly and is not difficult for the client to maintain between salon visits.

The true lie of the hair can be seen only when the hair is wet because certain styling techniques can disguise the direction of how the hair falls naturally. When you are looking at a head of hair to observe the natural hair growth patterns, you will need to comb the hair and pay particular attention to the following hair growth characteristics.

- nape hairline
- front hairline
- crown
- amount of root lift
- natural partings
- degree and uniformity of curl formation

Nape hairline

Situated at the back of the head, the nape hairline runs from ear to ear and is the perimeter of the hair growth on the neck. This line of hair growth will vary enormously between clients and men will usually have much lower hairlines at the nape. Some nape hairlines have particularly strong directions of growth and this can be limiting to what you can achieve with your scissors (or other cutting tools) so that the finished look lies properly. You will need to look for the direction and strength of the hair growth. Sometimes the direction of growth will be the same on both sides, being uniform and lying evenly. Other hairlines might have a tendency to grow towards one side while others may grow in opposite directions. A hairline which has both sides growing towards the centre is also common. The strength of the hair growth in this area will determine how you will cut the hair to achieve the best results. To see this properly you will need to comb the hair in this area in different directions (i.e. with and against the natural lie of the hair). If the hair is long and heavy, make sure that you are not deceived by the length of the hair weighing down the growth characteristics. Get all the unwanted hair out of the way so that you can clearly see which way the hair wants to lie on its own accord. You may find it easier to take very fine sections of hair, starting at the very bottom, and combing them to see the direction of growth and then gradually taking more hair until you have completed the observation.

Front hairline

Front hairlines are situated at the front of the head; they are the outermost growth of hair that runs from ear to ear across the forehead. Like hairlines at the back of the head, these vary a great deal between people and, in the case of male pattern baldness, can gradually alter during a lifetime. It is not until you start looking at front hairlines that you begin to appreciate how they differ between people. Some front hairlines will be virtually straight across while others will recede at the temples or grow close to the eyebrows at the temples. Some of these growth characteristics are determined by sex, age or ethnic group. For example, it is common for men to have receding hairlines and to have a lower growth of hair at the sides in front of the ears. Many Afro-Caribbean women have a lower hairline growth in front of their ears than European women. As people get older, the amount of hair on the head decreases and may begin to recede at the temples. Apart from the characteristics already described, the two other growth patterns you will encounter on a front hairline are cowlicks and widow's peaks. A cowlick is a strong area of hair growth in the opposite or an unusual direction at the front hairline. The hair will 'kick' out and the cowlick will be clearly visible. A widow's peak is a strong growth of hair where the hair grows into a peak and is usually at or very near to the centre of the front hairline. The front hairline of Count Dracula is an exaggerated example of a widow's peak.

Crown

The crown is situated at the top of the head but exact positions will vary. The crown determines the direction of hair growth on the top of the head and may be in the centre of the head, slightly to one side, high, low, or there might even be two of them! The term 'double crown' is used to describe a person who has two crowns. The hair at the crown might grow outwards from a visible point, sworling around in a strong circular pattern, while other crowns will be less distinct.

Amount of root lift

The angle at which the follicle is set in the skin determines a hair's direction of growth and also how close it will naturally lie to the skin. This is the 'root lift'. If the follicle is set in the skin at an acute angle, the hair will lie closer to the skin's surface than a hair emerging from a follicle that is set in the skin at, say, seventy degrees. The quantity and position of a person's follicles is determined at birth and does not alter throughout a lifetime. Although hair may not grow from every follicle for ever, the follicle is still present, as in the case of alopecia. The amount of root lift will vary in different areas of the head and between clients. If a client requires lift at the roots there are cutting techniques that can be used to help do this but results will depend upon how heavy the hair is. Sometimes perms are given to clients to help add lift and body at the roots.

Natural partings

A natural parting is the position of where the hair falls naturally between the crown area and the front hairline to form a break (parting) in the lie of the hair. Some natural partings will be at the side, while others may be in the centre or off centre. The old myth about partings being worn on one side if you are male and on the other side if you are female should be ignored. It is recommended that hairdressers style hair in accordance with a client's natural parting but we all know that this is not always possible because of the style the client wants. Therefore, you will often place partings elsewhere to achieve the desired look. Sometimes, working against the natural parting is useful for obtaining height in some styles, and the clever placing of a parting can make thin faces appear broader and wide faces appear narrower. A natural parting can be found only when the hair is wet. The hair is combed straight back from the face and using your free hand, the hair is gently nudged forward. The hair will then break to reveal the natural parting.

Degree and uniformity of curl formation

There is an expression that says we always want what we haven't got. Therefore people with straight hair often want it to be curly and vice versa. Ignoring natural curl and movement in the hair can often spoil a haircut, making it difficult for the client to manage and maintain. Working with any curl in the hair and using it to create the style is therefore recommended. If the curl in the client's hair is natural, it will probably be less curly when it is wet than when it has been wetted and allowed to dry naturally. However, if the curl was achieved chemically by perming, the hair has to be wet to see how much movement is present, because styling and drying methods can disguise the curl. The amount of movement in the hair might vary in different areas of the head. For example, the hair at the back may be less curly than the hair at the sides. If this is not spotted by you, it may result in the finished style not looking as it should.

How can these hair growth characteristics be controlled when cutting?

It is important to look for the natural hair fall and movement, and when possible, work so that they are incorporated into the haircut. Here are some useful examples of how the natural hair fall and movement can be used and controlled.

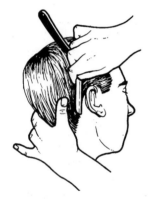

Figure 4.1 Hairline shaping using a razor

Nape hair growth

Try not to cut above the natural hairline at the nape when possible. Sometimes this will be necessary, and scissors, clippers or a razor can be used for this. Reshaping the hairline, or in other words, cutting the hair so that it takes on a shape different from the way it has grown, is most often done when fashion cutting, or cutting Afro-Caribbean or men's hair. (A word of warning about reshaping men's hairlines: if a man is very hairy, the hair on his neck may join into the hair growing on his back and it is very easy to get carried away removing the unwanted hair. Before you realise it, you can have cut away some of the hair that would not have been seen anyway, because it would be covered by a shirt!)

Certain hairline shapes lend themselves better to particular hair growth patterns. Refer back to Chapter 3 which discusses this in more detail.

The hairline may be reshaped using scissors, clippers or a razor. Examples are shown in Figures 4.1 and 4.2 (see also Figure 4.25, p. 81).

Figure 4.2 Hairline shaping using scissors

Front hairline

The growth characteristics you are most likely to encounter on the front hairline are cowlicks, widow's peaks and areas of recession. Cowlicks cause the hair to grow in a different direction to the rest of the hair on the hairline. It could cause the hair to move strongly to the left or right or perhaps push upwards. Try to use the direction of this movement in your cutting. If you attempt to cut a full fringe where a cowlick is present you will have difficulty because the fringe will kick out and appear uneven. If you use tension while cutting over a cowlick the result will be even more catastrophic. Tension will stretch the natural movement out of the hair and when the mesh of hair is released it will spring back and be surprisingly shorter than you anticipated. If the mesh is held with tension, and checked with the rest of the hair, it may appear to be technically correct and level, but as it is released, the ends will not be level.

Widow's peaks can also cause problems for the hairdresser. A widow's peak grows backwards from the face and trying to make the hair come forward onto the forehead should be avoided. That is to say, it is impossible to do this because it will very soon force itself back into its natural backward growing direction. Incidentally, did you know that the singer and actress Cher had electrolysis on her hairline to get rid of her widow's peak? This is proof in itself that there is nothing a hairdresser can do with their scissors to alter the way the hair grows naturally. Even if it is cut off down to the skin (as in the case of hairline reshaping) the hair will still grow back in the same direction.

If the hair recedes on the front hairline of a female client, she will probably want this to be disguised. This can also be said for many male clients too, especially if they are sensitive about any hair loss caused by male pattern baldness. If the client is concerned about concealing areas of recession, try to leave the hair slightly longer and heavier in these areas so that the hair can be styled to cover the balding area.

Crown

If your client has a double crown, you must avoid cutting the hair too short in this area. Cutting hair short on a double crown will cause the hair to stick straight out because there is no weight to hold it down. Try to leave the hair longer over double crowns to provide sufficient weight to stop it from sticking out like a brush.

Amount of root lift

There are cutting techniques that will increase the amount of lift at the roots. All of these techniques involve cutting selected strands of hair shorter than the overall length of the style. Short hair is stronger than long hair and will push up and away from the scalp creating lift and volume by supporting the hair lying over it. Special scissors are available that make texturising faster because there is no need to weave out the selected strands to be cut shorter since these scissors are notched. Only the hair where there are no notches in the scissor blades will be cut leaving the remaining hair that is closed in the scissors untouched. If the hair appears too full because the amount of hair is so dense, excess bulk can be removed by thinning scissors, which are very similar to the scissors used for texturising (see pp. 31–33).

How does the degree and uniformity of curl formation affect the choice of cutting technique?

When cutting curly hair you must remember that it will spring back when the mesh is released, and thus appear shorter. The greater the tension put on the curl, the more it will stretch to being straight. As soon as the tension is taken off the hair, it will spring back to being curly. Depending on the tightness of the curl and the style to be achieved, it might be necessary to cut the hair 'free-hand'. Free-hand cutting is a technique used for cutting fringes (Figure 4.3), over ears, on some hairlines and also natural Afro hair. It does not involve holding the hair between the fingers. Instead, the hair is first combed into the correct position to allow the hair to fall and lie naturally, then cut. Free-hand cutting does not put any tension on the hair at all, so allows the hairdresser to reduce its length without being fooled by the effect that tension has on hair fall and movement. If the hair is very straight, as in the case of most Chinese hair, free-hand cutting can also be used, allowing the hair to fall as gravity intends it to.

Figure 4.3 Cutting a fringe free hand

Basic cutting methods

Scissors can be used on wet or dry hair. Basically, there are three cutting methods that can be carried out, using different scissor techniques as well as razors or clippers. They are

- one length
- graduation
- layer.

Figure 4.4 One-length cut

One length

A one-length haircut would be described as the hair being cut to fall to the same outside length. The weight and fullness of the haircut is around the perimeter of the shape, while the inside hair has no shape or movement. For this reason (weight distribution), a one length haircut could be interpreted as having a slightly triangular appearance, due to the fullness achieved by the hair points ending at the same level, as shown in Figure 4.4.

Graduation

A graduated haircut is different from a one-length shape because the hair is held and cut at a specific angle to produce fullness blending into shorter lengths of hair. The weight and fullness of a graduated haircut moves up from the perimeter to a higher point and so has a slightly diamond shape, as shown in Figure 4.5.

Figure 4.5 Graduated cut

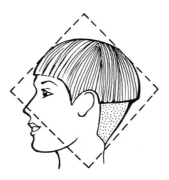

Layer

Layering reduces the hair length by holding and cutting the hair at an angle of 90 degrees to the shape of the head. The weight and fullness is evenly distributed, giving a round appearance to the style, as shown in Figure 4.6.

It is not unusual to use more than one cutting method on a single head. Try looking at some style plates in trade magazines and see if you can work out how each was cut.

Figure 4.6 Layer cut

What effects can be achieved by different cutting angles and lines?

The angle at which the hair is cut to create different shapes and lines is limited only by your own imagination, technical skill and the particular head you are working on. Here are some examples of different cutting angles.

Nape outline shapes (Figure 4.7)

When deciding on the cutting angle which forms the shape at the nape, remember to look closely at the natural hair growth characteristics before beginning to cut.

Side outline shapes (Figure 4.8)

It is helpful to 'plot' the angle of your cutting line using features of the face. For example, you can imagine a line which runs to the nose or corner

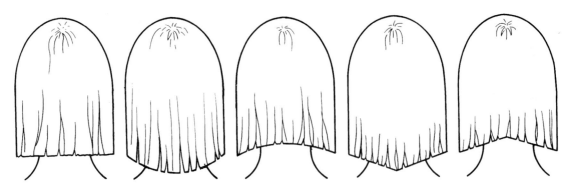

Figure 4.7 Nape outline shapes

Figure 4.8 Side outline shapes

of the eye from the chin, and use this imaginary line to help cut at the correct angle.

Fringe outline shapes (Figure 4.9)

If the hair is to be cut into a fringe, do check the hair growth pattern around the front hairline and the client's facial characteristics so that the most suitable shape is chosen.

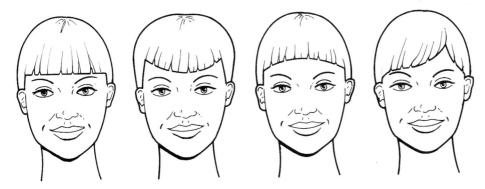

Figure 4.9 Fringe outline shapes

Geometric shapes (Figure 4.10)

Geometric styles are hair shapes which have been cut on lines to resemble angular shapes. They were made popular by Vidal Sassoon, in the 1960s, who created the 'five point' haircut for fashion designer Mary Quant (who designed and introduced the mini skirt).

Figure 4.10 Geometric shapes

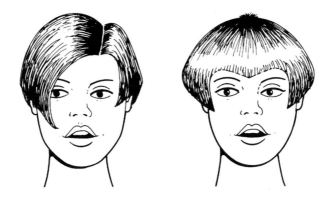

Asymmetric shapes (Figure 4.11)

The word asymmetric describes a shape that is unequal in line or size on both sides. (A shape which is equal in line or size on both sides is called symmetrical.)

Figure 4.11 Asymmetric shapes

Why is the balance and proportion of a haircut important?

There are two ways in which a haircut should be checked for balance and proportion. First, the haircut should be *technically correct*. That means, the hair should be cut so that the hair lengths check into each other and do not show signs of disconnection or difference in length. Regardless of the shape of the haircut, or the method by which it was done, the style should always be checked during the haircut, when the cut is complete, and after the style is dried. If the haircut is not technically correct, the style will not be easy to manage for the client and could show the imperfections when it is finished. Second, the haircut should be correctly balanced and proportioned to the size and shape of the body and the facial characteristics. Too many hairdressers forget the importance of the total look. You will see clients standing up when their hairdresser has finished, and as they take off the gown, the style just does not look right. The haircut may be perfection in terms of technical skill but if it does not balance with, and therefore complement, the client's facial characteristics, you have not done justice to your client.

How is the balance of a haircut checked?

If you are cutting a one-length style, such as a bob, you are going to be concentrating on checking that the lines are equally level on all sides. A one-length cut always shows any imperfections because the outside shape is so defined and strong. Do not be under the misapprehension that clients will not become aware of any mistakes. If they do not notice the imperfection while they are in the salon, you can guarantee that it will be noticed when they dry it themselves at home.

A one-length shape can be checked by taking a small amount of hair in your hands from either side of the head at equal places and slowly sliding you fingers down the hair. If the hair is the same length on both sides, you hands will reach the points of the hair at the same time. It is not a good idea to try to check the balance by using the ears as a guide because they are very rarely equally positioned. To check the base line (outside edge) of a short bob, a hand mirror can be placed under the hairline to reflect any imperfections. You could also ask your client to stand up so that you have an eye-level view for checking the cut.

When checking all other haircuts, you have a little more work to do because unlike a one-length style, you have an outside and inside shape to check. It can be helpful to use the mirrors around the salon to check the shape of your cut from different angles and distances, because it is often easier to identify any discord or disproportion from a distance than it is close up. The client's hair or head can also be turned so that the haircut is seen more closely by picking up meshes of hair to see if the ends of the hair are level. If they are not, the stray strands are cut off. To check that the weight is evenly balanced, the fingers can be drawn through the hair in an outwards direction from roots to points. By looking in the mirror you will be able to see if any area has been left too long.

One-length (bob) cutting

It is argued that a one-length style is one of the most difficult to cut. This is because the stylist must ensure that the line is exactly balanced. There is no room for errors when cutting a bob because mistakes will always show.

Verelle Hairdressing – step by step

Step 1
Long, fine hair has been shampooed and is ready for cutting.

Step 2
The hair is divided into two main sections by making a parting from the front hairline to the nape of the neck. The stylist combs a narrow mesh of hair so that it is flat against the skin and cuts the guideline.

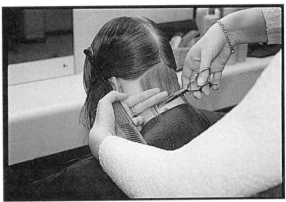

Step 3
Another section of hair is taken and the guideline underneath can clearly be seen. The stylist cuts this mesh of hair precisely to the guideline.

Step 4
The stylist continues to take narrow meshes of hair working up towards the crown. Notice how the stylist uses her fingers to check that both sides are of equal length.

Step 5

When the stylist has reached just below the crown, she takes her next mesh of hair to include the hair at the sides. The guideline at the back is followed through to the sides. It is important not to use any undue tension on the hair over the ear because when the tension is released, the hair resting over the ear will be shorter.

Step 6

The stylist repeats this on the other side and again checks that the haircut is even.

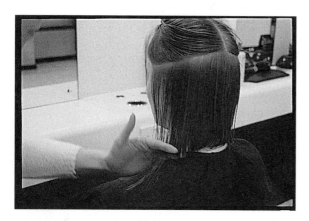 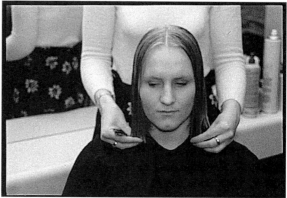

Step 7

A triangular section is made on the front hairline to cut the fringe. If cutting the hair wet, remember that hair will appear shorter when it is dried.

Step 8

The finished haircut.

Step 9
The haircut after blow-drying.

Graduation cutting

1 A freshly coloured head of hair is ready for cutting.
2 This haircut begins at the side of the head where the main bulk of the hair will fall, i.e. *not* the side of the head where the parting is positioned. All the hair from the parting is brought down and held closely to the head. In this example, the hair is held so that the angle of cutting is equivalent to the width of the hairdresser's middle finger.
3 This cutting line is continued to just behind the ear.
4 The cutting line can be clearly seen, showing the underneath hair which will be removed using the scissors over comb technique.
5 The underneath hair is cut by positioning the comb close to the contours of the head. The hair which protrudes through the teeth of the comb is cut off. The cutting line which is creating an area of weight is continued from behind the ears through the occipital region.

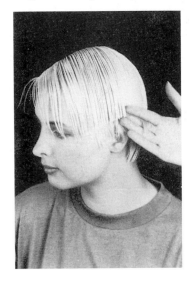

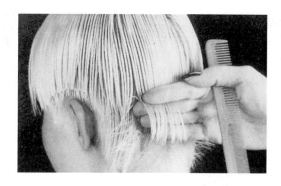 

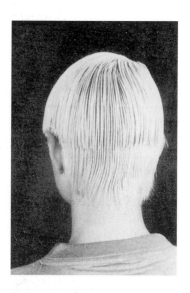 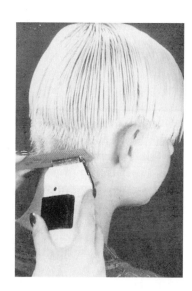 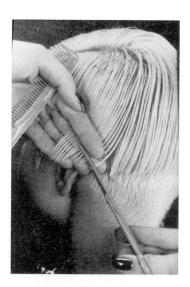

6 This photograph shows the completed cutting line at the back of the head.

7 The hair below the weight line is removed by using electric clippers. The comb is used to lift and hold the hair for cutting in the same way as for scissors over comb.

8 The side of the head where the parting is placed can now be cut. Notice that the cutting line is sloped up towards the eye.

9 The front hair is cut to blend the shortest hair at the parting, to the longest point over the other eye.

10 To add interest in the crown area, the hair is cut shorter to prevent it from being too flat.

11 This shorter area is blended into the rest of the hair by angling the fingers so that minimum length is removed from the weight line.

12 Point cutting through the crown area will reduce the bulk, giving the hair a more textured appearance.

13 Side view of the completed cut before it is dried.

14 The hair has been blow-dried to create a sleek finish.

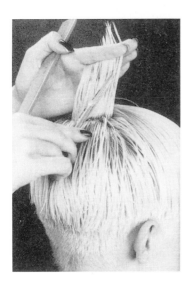 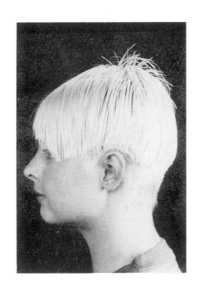 

(Photographs reproduced courtesy of Goldwell)

Layer cutting

1 Freshly permed hair ready for cutting.
2 Beginning at the nape, the guideline is cut with the hair held next to the skin.
3 The guideline is cut so that it curves up towards the ears. Narrow, horizontal sections are taken, and all the back hair is cut to the same guideline.
4 Using horizontal sections, the hair at the sides is blended with the guideline at the back. The hair is cut at an angle so that the longest point is level with the chin.
5 When both sides have been cut, the outside shape in the temporal area is blended with the longest point at the chin.
6 The hair on the front hairline, across the forehead, is cut by making 'V' shaped snips with the points of the scissors to achieve a textured finish.
7 When the outside shape is finished, the internal layering is carried out. Taking a vertical section in the centre back of the head, the mesh is held straight out from the head. The guide for cutting the layers is taken from the shortest point seen in the hairdresser's fingers, i.e. the hair nearest to the client's nape.

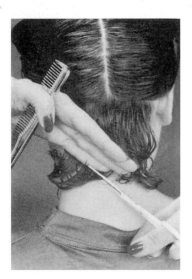
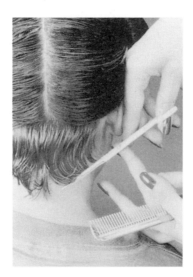

8 Once cut, this mesh of hair will act as the guideline for all the internal layering. The sections are held at a 90 degree angle for this cutting technique. Remember that the angle at which the hair is cut is achieved by holding the meshes at right angles to the contours of the head.
9 The final shape is an easy to manage style that can be scrunch-dried using a hair dryer with a diffuser attachment.
10 In this photograph, the hair has been dried with the fingers and then tonged to create the deep waves.

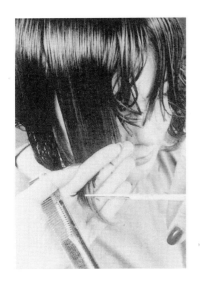

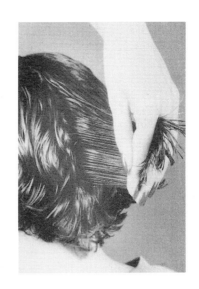

(Photographs reproduced courtesy of Goldwell)

Club cutting

Club cutting is also referred to as blunt cutting; this cutting technique reduces the length of hair by making straight cuts with the scissor blades. The points of the hair are left the same length and blunt. Club cutting is used today more than any other technique and is ideal for fine hair because it helps to make such hair feel and look heavier. Electric clippers can also be used to club cut the hair as shown in Figure 4.12, which shows hair being cut with the aid of a 'Flattoper'.

Figure 4.12 Club cutting with clippers. Here a special comb, the Brian Drumm Flattopper, is used to support and lift the hair so that it remains perfectly level for cutting. A spirit level in the handle lets the hairdresser know if it is being held straight (Courtesy Brian Drumm)

Taper cutting

There are two cutting tools that can be used to taper cut hair: scissors or a razor. Taper cutting with scissors should be carried out on dry hair while a razor is used only on wet hair. Taper cutting removes length from the hair *and at the same time* removes bulk. The thinning effect of tapering creates shorter lengths of hair among each mesh. This results in each mesh being progressively finer towards the points, and this is responsible for increasing the hair's natural tendency to curl. The effect of taper cutting a mesh of hair can be seen in Figure 4.13.

Figure 4.13 Taper cut mesh showing progressive reduction of bulk towards points (a) before cutting (b) after cutting

(a)

Before cutting

(b)

After cutting

Taper cutting with scissors is also referred to as slithering or feathering the hair. The scissors are used in a sliding action, backwards and forwards along the hair length. The heel of the scissors is used when tapering and the cutting occurs during the upward stroke of the blades, as they very slightly close on the hair. The method of holding a mesh of hair when taper cutting with scissors is shown in Figure 4.14.

Figure 4.14 Taper cutting with scissors

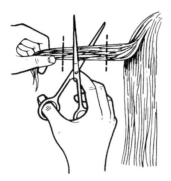

Razor cutting techniques

Taper cutting with a razor

When using a razor to taper cut, it is placed either underneath or above the mesh of hair to be cut. The hair is held and the razor blade is stroked down the hair in a scraping action from the middle lengths to the ends. Do be careful how much pressure you put on the blade; more pressure will remove a lot more hair! While razor cutting, both hands should move in unison. The hand holding the mesh moves away as the blade approaches – an important movement to remember to avoid cutting your fingers. The blade is *always* moved towards you, *never* towards the scalp and against the lie of the cuticle. This is shown in Figure 4.15.

Figure 4.15 Taper cutting with a razor: the razor is placed either underneath or above the mesh of hair to be cut

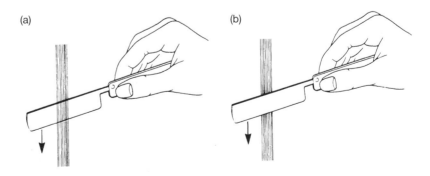

(a)   (b)

Club cutting with a razor

Unlike taper cutting with a razor, the blade is held at a right angle towards the mesh, as illustrated in Figure 4.16. The mesh must be held taut so that the blade edge can slice through to achieve a clubbed cut. The actual cut is made between the fingers and the head, not directly over the fingers, using the same angles and positions of the hair as for club cutting using scissors.

Figure 4.16 Club cutting with a razor

Thinning and texturising techniques

Thinning

This is a term given to cutting techniques which remove bulk from the hair *without* affecting the overall length of the style. Conventional scissors or razors can be used although special thinning scissors are available with notched teeth instead of solid blades. Thinning scissors are also referred to as aescalups and can have one or both blades notched. If both blades are notched, *less* hair will be removed than a pair with only one notched blade. This can be seen in Figure 4.17 which shows a magnified view of the two types of thinning scissors.

Figure 4.17 The amount of hair cut with (a) double notch (b) single notch thinning scissors

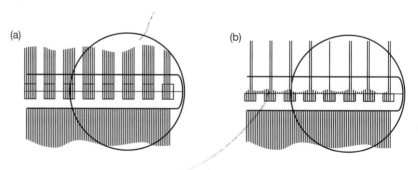

Thinning scissors should be used on dry hair and are held in the same way as conventional haircutting scissors (i.e. with the thumb and third finger). A mesh of hair is held between the fingers and the scissors are closed across the mesh at least 4 cm from the scalp. At this distance, you will prevent spiky hair sticking up through the top layers when the hair is combed flat. The scissors are closed once and then opened and moved down another 2–3 cm and another cut is made. If the hair is very long or dense, you will need to continue this movement down the length of the hair until the excess bulk is removed, but be careful not to remove too much hair. Use the finely spaced teeth of your comb to remove the cuttings from the mesh while thinning, as this will help you to estimate how many times the scissors will need to be closed. When using thinning scissors on men, they are usually used straight across the hair mesh as shown in Figure 4.18 while for women's hairdressing they are generally used at an angle or in a zig-zag pattern.

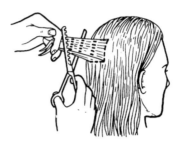

Figure 4.18 Using thinning scissors (aescalups)

Avoid using thinning scissors in the following areas:

- closer than 4 cm to the scalp
- on hairlines
- at the crown
- along partings.

Razors can also be used to thin out the hair but must only ever be used on wet hair because razor cutting dry hair would quickly blunt the razor and be painful for the client. To ensure that the overall length of the hair is not altered, minimum pressure is put on the razor as it is stroked over the mesh of hair towards you. The blade should be held flat to the hair when using a razor to remove excess bulk.

Texturising

This is a cutting technique which involves cutting selected strands of hair shorter than the overall style length with the intention of increasing root lift or softening a hard line. It can be done using specialised scissors or, as it is done more commonly, with conventional scissors. Unlike thinning, texturising is usually intended to show visible variations between hair lengths. Here are some examples of texturising techniques.

Weave cutting

The weave cutting technique (Figure 4.19) works on the principle that the hairs which are cut shorter will push up and support the longer lengths – ideal for those hairstyles which need to be spiky or have a 'strand' appearance. The width between the weaving should be evenly spaced. To achieve heavy texturising, the strands are woven out thickly and, for a

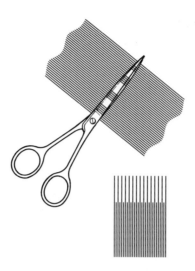

Figure 4.19 Weave cutting, using closed scissors to weave out selected strands; the result is shown below: shorter hairs are evenly dispersed among the longer ones

more subtle look, the strands are finer. Weave cutting can be carried out over the whole head but is time-consuming because such narrow meshes (about 1 cm) are used. Therefore, weave cutting is usually restricted to specific areas.

Chipping and pointing

Chipping and pointing reduce the weight from the points of the hair to create an uneven or jagged finish by cutting small 'V' shapes into the points. They can be used to soften or spike any area of a style, including fringes. Figure 4.20 shows how to hold sections vertically and point: this can be done all over the head, removing as much bulk as required.

Figure 4.20 Vertical point cutting technique using conventional scissors (Courtesy Rand Rocket Ltd)

Twisting and tapering

By twisting small strands of hair and then using the taper cutting technique (as shown in Figure 4.21), it is possible to remove length and bulk. The shorter hairs will provide root lift while the longer hairs which this technique leaves will have a feathered appearance. (See p. 72 for taper cutting.)

Figure 4.21 Twisting and tapering strands of hair to create interesting texture (Courtesy Vidal Sassoon)

Scissors over comb technique

This technique was called shingling when it was at the height of its popularity between the First and Second World Wars (1920s and 1930s). Today, the term 'scissors over comb' describes hair being cut close to the contours of the head and is mostly used at the nape or sides of the head. A thin, flexible comb is needed so that the hair can be cut as close to the contours of the head as required. The comb is used in an upwards direction, lifting the hair as it moves through the hair. The scissors are held parallel with the comb all the time and your hands should move in unison with each other, in a flowing movement. As the hairs slip through the teeth of the comb they are cut off. This can be seen in Figure 4.22.

Figure 4.22 Scissors over comb technique (Courtesy Vidal Sassoon)

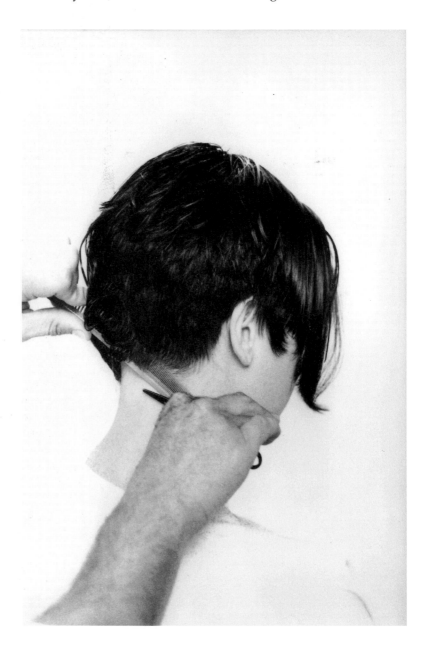

Electric clippers are often used instead of clippers to cut hair close to the head as shown in Figure 4.23. Clippers are generally used instead of scissors for this purpose when cutting Afro hair.

Figure 4.23 Clipper over comb technique

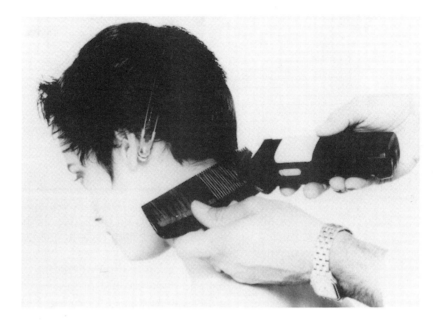

Removing split ends

Fragilitis crinium or, as it is more commonly known, split ends, cannot be permanently repaired by the use of conditioners. The only treatment to get rid of the split ends is to cut them off. However, clients should be consulted about the way they treat their hair and the products that they use because something has caused the hair to split. If the reason for the damage can be identified, clients can be educated about how they should care for their hair to prevent future damage.

Clients will need to be given a conditioning treatment to nourish the middle lengths and ends of their hair, to make them less brittle and then have the split ends cut off. Sometimes, the hair will be split quite a long way up the hair shaft. If the affected hairs are not cut, the splitting can continue up the entire length of the hair. Cutting off split ends does not necessarily mean that clients must have their hair cut very short. The hairdresser can remove the affected parts of the hair without altering the overall appearance of the hairstyle. This is done by taking meshes of hair about 3 cm square and twisting the hair from the scalp to the points. By running the thumb and forefinger up the twist of hair towards the scalp, the split ends will stand out. Starting at the root end, you can begin cutting off the split ends with the points of your scissors, working towards the hair points. This is shown in Figure 4.24, and is carried out on any part of the head where the hair is split when the hair is dry.

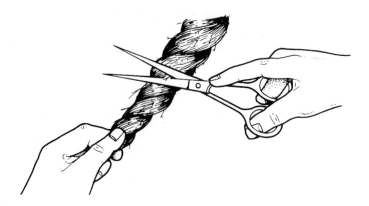

Figure 4.24 Cutting off split ends from a twist of hair

Shaping hairlines

Hair is usually cut while it is wet after shampooing. Most texturising and thinning techniques are carried out when the hair has naturally dried out during the haircut, being easily redampened by a water spray for blow-drying, setting or perming.

Although a prior examination of the hair and scalp and discussion between stylist and client should precede any hairdressing service, it is much easier to see the true lie of the hair (i.e. hair growth patterns) when the hair is wet. This is because styling methods often distort the natural lie of the hair and force it into opposite directions. For example, clients may part their hair on the side they have worn the parting since childhood, but it may be the opposite side to where the parting falls naturally.

Generally speaking, a style should work with the growth patterns of the hair so that it falls and moves in the direction that it grows naturally. By working to this formula, the style will be manageable and lasting. A cowlick on the front hairline can be a problem if the stylist tries to conceal it. As it is a strong growth of hair growing in an opposite or unusual direction, it is not easily hidden. It is better practice to make the cowlick a feature of the haircut, by using the strong growth pattern for movement and direction.

The direction of hair cannot be altered by anything the hairdresser can do, as it is determined by the hair follicle, where our skills and products cannot reach. Therefore, cutting the hair to the same level as the skin surface will not make it grow back in a different direction, or indeed grow any thicker, faster or darker. Occasionally, it may be necessary to create a false hairline for a client whose hairline is either the wrong shape, or grows too weakly for the intended look. It may be that there are just a few hairs which grow too low for the style at the nape. This is very often carried out on Afro-Caribbean hair designs to create a strong, geometric shape on hairlines which are weak at the sides, nape and front.

Three different tools can be used when hairline shaping:

- clippers
- razor
- scissors.

Great care should be taken to observe any pimples or other raised areas of skin which could be caught by the cutting tool. Always use a neck brush to brush away all hair clippings continually.

Hairline shaping using clippers

There are many different types of hair clippers, but for this type of work an extremely fine blade is necessary so that it cuts close to the skin. Some clippers have adjustable blades while others may have interchangeable blades. The size of blade recommended for hairline shaping is 0000, which is equivalent to 0.1 mm. The clippers are directed against the natural lie of the hair towards the outline shape of the style as shown in Figure 4.25. A line can be made with the very edge of the clippers to mark out the new shape before cutting. When shaping the front hairline with clippers, cover the client's eyes with tissue to prevent small hair clippings from entering the eyes.

Figure 4.25 Hairline shaping using electric clippers

Hairline shaping using a razor

The skin must be made wet and lubricated with a shaving cream or foam to help the razor glide close to the skin and facilitate the cutting of the hair. Any pimples or raised areas should be marked by removing the cream or foam so that they are left exposed (never rely on memory!). The razor is rested against the skin and brought down in a stroking movement while keeping the head still and the skin taut (see Figure 4.1, p. 58). This takes considerable care and skill.

Hairline shaping using scissors

It usually takes longer to carry out hairline shaping using scissors than it does with clippers, but women do not usually like the idea of having their hairline clippered or shaved. This probably comes from the myth that hair cut in this way grows back coarser and darker. The outline shape of the hairline is first cut with the scissors (see Figure 4.2, p. 58), and then the unwanted hair below this line is cut away by resting the blades flat on the skin and opening and closing quickly, moving only the blade operated by the thumb. When carrying out this fast cutting action, the skin should be stretched taut to avoid cutting the client's neck. This is especially necessary when dealing with older clients whose skin is looser and more wrinkled.

Technical cutting tips

- During a haircut, stand away from your client occasionally as it is easier to identify any discord or disproportion from a distance.
- Use a vent brush to brush hair in different directions during a haircut so that you can see how well the hair is falling and any imperfections can be seen and corrected.
- Keep a water spray close at hand to redampen the hair during cutting if necessary.

- Work with the growth of the hair – not against it.
- Use the mirrors around the salon to check the shape of your haircut from different angles and distances.
- To check the base line of a short bob, a hand mirror can be placed under the hairline to reflect any imperfections.
- When checking an Afro haircut stand at your client's side and slowly tilt the head away from you and then back again, keeping your eye on the outline shape.
- Keep your sections narrow so that the cutting line of the previous mesh can clearly be seen.
- Do not use tension on the hair when cutting over the ear. Make allowances for the degree of ear protrusion by allowing the hair to fall naturally and cutting free hand in this area.
- Incorporate different cutting techniques in a style to achieve interesting and personalised hair designs.
- Remember that hair stretches more when it is wet so it will appear shorter when it has dried.

Technical tips for cutting Afro-Caribbean hair

- Spray hair with instant moisturiser to make the hair easier to comb.
- Use clippers to shape and clean hairlines.
- Allow for the greater elastic recoil (spring) of Afro-Caribbean hair than is present in other types of hair.
- When cutting natural Afro-Caribbean hair (hair which has not been chemically relaxed or permed), continually lift out the hair with an Afro comb or pick to ensure the balance and shape is correctly proportioned.
- Avoid the use of razors on Afro-Caribbean hair as they splice the hair which can cause it to split and fray.

Cutting children's hair

The techniques and procedures for cutting children's hair are basically the same as those for adults and adolescents. There are some differences, however, so stylists should be aware of the following:

- hair texture
- haircare
- child behaviour
- style lines.

Hair texture

Babies are born with soft, downy hair which will last only between one and four years before it is replaced with slightly coarser hair. The first 'baby hair' is often a different colour from the hair that replaces it and may also be more curly. The stylist should therefore inform the parent of the child that the curls may not return once cut.

Haircare

If the hair is to be cut while wet, use a low pH shampoo, and if possible, one which will not sting the eyes if it should accidentally come into contact with them (baby shampoo). Conditioner is not normally necessary because their hair will not have been abused at a young age.

Never carry out any form of chemical treatment on a child such as perming, tinting, bleaching or relaxing. The risks are too great for any stylist.

Cut the hair so that it will dry naturally and fall easily into place; parents do not want to have to style the hair with blow-driers or tongs each time it is washed. Always check for the presence of nits, as these are very common among young children.

Child behaviour

The first haircut a child has can be an extremely traumatic experience if enough patience, consideration and care are not taken. The child should visit the salon with the mother beforehand so that the salon becomes a familiar environment and the staff are not strangers. The child will be fascinated by what is going on, will see mother having her hair cut, shampooed, etc., and see that she enjoys it.

When the child eventually visits the salon for the first haircut, the stylist must be friendly. Call the child by his or her first name or nickname as it will help the child to relax. A little bribery in the form of a small present or sweets works wonders!

Once the child is in the chair, make sure he or she is comfortable and that there is something to amuse them. Some salons have specially fitted out areas with chairs made to look like animals and have cartoons running on a video, with bright pictures on the walls.

Leave children's hands free from underneath the gown so that they feel less confined and can amuse themselves with, perhaps, a small toy. Always treat the hair gently; any pulling will upset the child. If you plan to wet the hair using a spray gun, show the child how it works before using it. The same applies to the action of the scissors because it is often the noise of the scissor blades when they close that frightens children.

The biggest problem that a stylist faces is the child's inability to sit still. Try to carry out the haircut as quickly as possible and use your hand to steady the head by gently holding the chin or nape of the neck. Try to keep hair clippings from falling on the face and always balance your scissors and practise caution when shaping fringes and around the ears. Children have a natural tendency to make sudden, unexpected movements. Avoid any sudden movements yourself which might frighten them.

Style lines

Simple styles that follow the natural hair growth pattern are best for children because the hair will retain its shape throughout the day. Fringes are particularly popular for young children.

Blunt (club) cutting is recommended for children's hair because it helps make the hair look thicker and gives the ends more body. Razor cutting children's hair is not recommended as usually they do not like the slight dragging sensation caused by the razor. Thinning scissors or texturising techniques can be used on children's hair if it is particularly dense.

If the hair is long, spend some time showing the parent how different styles can be achieved, such as ponytails, plaits, bunches, etc. Also show how to use and place slides and ribbons. A warning about traction alopecia would not be amiss.

Safe working guidelines

- Ensure cutting tools are clean and sterile.
- Check that electric clippers are safe to use and in good working order.
- Politely ask clients to remove bulky sweaters, earrings or scarves that might cause a hazard or impede your ability to cut the hair.
- Ensure clients are adequately gowned.
- Consider your client's comfort by using a neck brush to remove hair clippings *during* a haircut to prevent skin irritation and fidgeting.
- Sweep up the hair clippings immediately after the haircut is finished as it makes floors hazardous to walk on and looks untidy.
- If free-hand cutting, particularly near the face or eyes, ask your client to close their eyes and to remain still. Steady your scissors with your other hand as you cut to maintain maximum control of your movements. (Please note, this technique is not recommended for cutting children's hair because they may suddenly move.)
- When removing unwanted hair on a hairline with scissors, stretch the skin so that it is taut as this will help reduce the risk of cutting the client. This is particularly important for older clients whose skin has lost it elasticity.
- Do not keep any sharp objects in your pockets. In fact, it is unhygienic to put *any* hairdressing tools in your pockets.
- If you need to dispose of any sharp objects such as razor blades, either put them into a proper sharps box or place in old screw top jar before they are put in the dustbin.
- If you should cut yourself...
  - excuse yourself from your client
  - apply pressure to the wound with cotton wool or tissue to help stop the blood flow
  - apply a plaster or other suitable dressing to the wound
  - put the soiled piece of cotton wool or tissue in a bag before putting in the dustbin
  - sterilise the tool which caused the cut.

If the cut is severe, you may require stitches and a tetanus injection. You would also need to make a record of the incident in the salon's accident book.

- If you should cut a client...
  - do not ignore it, but apologise immediately
  - ask the *client* to apply pressure to the wound using either a piece of cotton wool or tissue – do not allow the blood to come into contact with you

- if necessary, cover the wound with a suitable dressing
- ask the client to drop the soiled piece of cotton wool or tissue into a bag (do not touch it yourself) and dispose of the bag in the dustbin
- sterilise the tool which caused the cut.
- If you need to clean up a blood spillage…
  - wear protective gloves
  - pour undiluted household bleach onto the blood
  - use tissue or an old cloth to mop up the blood
  - place the soiled tissue or cloth and your gloves in a bag and put it in the dustbin
  - wash your hands.

Step-by-step fashion cutting techniques

Trevor Sorbie – step by step

This series of step-by-step photographs shows how Trevor Sorbie creates texture in a short head of hair, achieving interesting movement and varying hair length for a short tousled look.

Step 1 Ordinary cutting scissors are used for this haircut to reduce the length and to create the texture. Starting at the front, the hair is cut to about 4 cm long. Using the points of the scissors the hair is chopped to achieve a variation in length and less weight at the ends of the hair. (Photographs courtesy of Trevor Sorbie)

Step 2 Working towards the crown, the sections are taken the same as in step 1, reducing the bulk on the ends and creating texture by chopping into the hair.

Step 3 Arriving at the crown, the overall length should be approximately 4–5 cm.

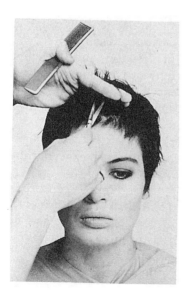
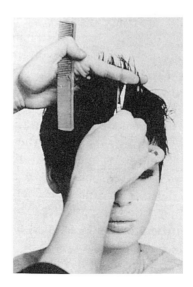

Step 4 The sides should be cut to approximately 2–3 cm long. Again, the points of the scissors are used to cut into the ends of the hair to create texture.

Step 5 Now working into the back area, the hair is cut short into the nape.

 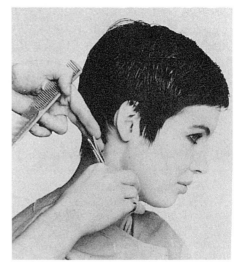

Step 6 The hair at the hairline is cut into a solid V shape.

Step 7 Returning to the front, the hair is combed down onto the forehead. Using the free-hand cutting technique (i.e. not holding the hair in the fingers) the hair is cut to leave a random cut look.

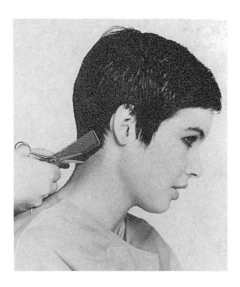 

Step 8 The sides are cut using the same technique as used for the fringe.

Step 9 Extra strength mousse is applied to give a fuller and more tousled effect and it is dried using the fingers.

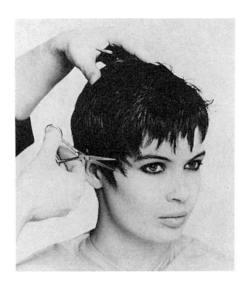 

Cheynes Artistic Team – step by step

Step 1 One-length, a medium thick hair with slight natural movement and highlights. The new look will be mid-length and layered with longer lengths through the front.

Step 2 After shampooing, the hair is combed cleanly back from a centre parting and cut straight across in one section to achieve the base line.

Step 3 Hair is held up to 90 degrees through top section working from front hairline to crown to achieve a square layer.

  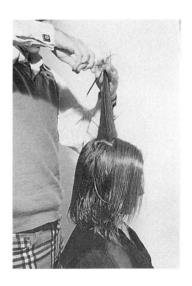

Step 4 The sides are brought up to crown and cut to the square.

Step 5 This shows the squared layering completed.

Step 6 Vertical sections are taken from the crown to the base line and the hair is cut to remove weight. The sections are taken from the crown working towards the ears. The back is cross-checked by holding the hair in the opposite direction.

  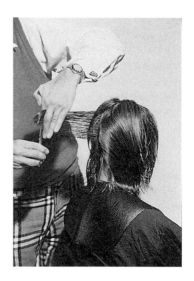

Step 7 This shows the back hair completed.

Step 8 A narrow section is taken (approximately 2 cm) at the front hairline and a razor is used to taper cut the front shape.

Step 9 The ends of the front hair are then thinned by gently stroking the razor against the ends of the hair.

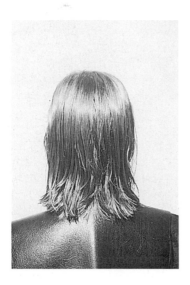 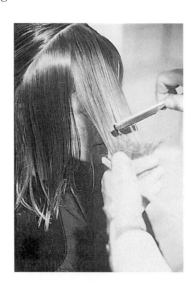 

Step 10 This shows the completed front shape.

Step 11 The front shape is matched with the back base line.

Step 12 Horizontal sections are taken through the back, starting at the occipital area, and a razor is used to remove excess bulk from the ends of the hair to encourage movement and increase texture.

Step 13 The razor is used on the back sections which work up towards the crown.

Step 14 At the crown, 2 cm square sections are taken and the ends are tapered with the razor to break up the weight.

Step 15 The base line is pointed into with the tips of the scissors to complete the design.

  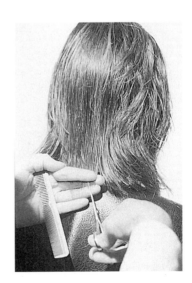

Step 16 Mousse is applied and the hair is blow-dried using the fingers. After the hair was dried, serum was applied to achieve optimum shine.

Step 17 The finished look.

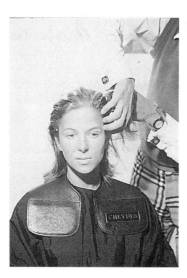

1   Give two reasons why hair should be cut according to the natural lie of the hair.

2   Can the true lie of the hair best be seen before or after shampooing?

3   Name two types of hair growth patterns found on front hairlines.

4   What is a double crown?

5   What determines the natural root lift of hair?

6   How is a client's natural parting found?

7   What are the three main methods of cutting hair?

8   Make diagrams to show three different nape outline shapes for one-length styles.

9   Make diagrams to show three different side outline shapes for one-length styles.

10 Make diagrams to show three different fringe outline shapes.

11 What cutting tools can be used for club cutting hair?

12 What is another name to describe club cutting?

13 Does club cutting remove bulk from the points of the hair?

14 Which cutting tools can be used to taper cut hair?

15 Which cutting tool should be used only on wet hair?

16 Which cutting technique increases the hair's natural tendency to curl?

17 Is it true that taper cutting removes bulk and length from the hair?

18 When cutting hair with a razor, should the razor be stroked down the hair towards the points or upwards towards the roots?

19 What is another name for thinning scissors?

20 Does thinning affect the overall length of the hair?

21 List four areas where thinning is not recommended.

22 Why should minimal pressure be used if using a razor to thin hair?

23 Will thinning scissors with one plane and one notched blade remove more or less hair than a pair of thinning scissors with two notched blades?

24 Name two texturising techniques.

25 What cutting technique is used to create a style which is very short at the nape or sides of the head?

26 Describe how split ends are removed.

27 What cutting tools can be used to shape hairlines?

28 Does hair stretch most when it is wet or dry?

29 Why should the use of razors be avoided on Afro-Caribbean hair?

30 Why should hair clippings be swept up when a haircut is completed?

31 If removing unwanted hair on the neckline with scissors, why should the skin be stretched so that it is taut?

32 How should you dispose of sharp objects, such as razor blades?

33 Explain why it is sometimes necessary to ask clients to remove bulky sweaters, scarves and earrings.

34 What should be applied to a cut to help stop the blood flow?

35 What should be poured onto a blood spillage before it is cleaned up?

Advanced Questions

1 Explain the styling limitations which each of the following hair growth patterns may present:

(i) cowlick

(ii) widow's peak

(iii) double crown

(iv) low napeline with an upward growth pattern

2 Describe, with the aid of diagrams, the procedure for cutting a one-length shape.

3 Describe the effect of each of the following haircutting techniques and give an example of when each would be used:

(i) removing bulk with thinning scissors

(ii) taper cutting hair using a razor

(iii) scissors over comb

(iv) shaping a hairline using electric clippers or a razor

4 With the aid of diagrams, describe three texturising techniques and their effect on the hair.

5 Describe the procedures which should be followed in these situations:

(i) cutting yourself

(ii) cutting the client

(iii) cleaning up a blood spillage

Chapter 5

SETTING

Introduction

Setting involves a temporary physical change in the structure of hair. This change is achieved by wet hair being stretched around a roller, secured and dried. Of course, you do not necessarily need to use a conventional roller to create movement in hair as it can be successfully positioned around other 'moulds' to produce an interesting range of effects. Wet hair can also be moulded into a shape and dried as in finger waving and pincurling, or positioned around a hairbrush as is the case during blow-drying. The degree and type of movement introduced into the hair will depend upon the size and shape of the rollers used (or other form) and where and how they are positioned in the hair.

Hair can be set to make the hair straighter, more curly, fuller, flatter, sleeker or more wavy. All these effects can be achieved simply by the setting methods which the operator chooses to use and the imaginative way the rollers or whatever are positioned.

It is very disheartening to go into a salon and see a row of women sitting under hood driers with their hair set in exactly the same way. Do they all go out of the salon looking the same? Too often, hairdressers put in rollers in a mundane pattern with little or no thought given to the finished look or how the client will manage it at home. Do these hairdressers realise that they are in fact making their task more difficult? If you place rollers in a different position from the way you intend to dress it, or course you are going to meet problems. Some stylists frantically backcomb trying to dress the hair so that it takes on a decent shape. If only these hairdressers realised how much better the quality of their work would be if they practised the basic skill of setting hair. Such hairdressers do not become champion hairdressers nor fashion innovators. They are quite satisfied with their standard of work because they usually do not know any better. What is disturbing, though, is that these people will often be responsible for training others. With the competition of other salons and hairdressers operating in your area you cannot afford *not* to be able to set hair well. If you cannot do something a client requests, or you do it badly, there is always a hairdresser who can do it well and will take that client from you.

As the change to the hair during setting is physical, the effect is easily reversed when the hair is subjected to moisture because hair is hygroscopic. Hygroscopic describes a substance which has the ability to absorb moisture from the atmosphere. Consequently, clients will find their set is weakened or completely lost if they are caught in a shower of rain or spend a long time in a steamy bathroom without protecting their hair. The physical change to the hair during setting (or blow-drying) is known as a cohesive set.

Chemistry of the cohesive set

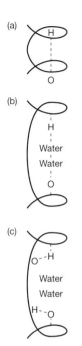

Figure 5.1 (a) Hair in its unstretched state **(b)** bound water enters the hair as it stretches **(c)** during drying water is evaporated off and the hair is held in its stretched state when bonds are formed in different positions

As the setting of hair relies on its ability to stretch, it can be carried out really successfully only on hair that is in good condition. The stretching of dry hair is controlled to a great extent by weak, but numerous, hydrogen bonds. Because there are millions of these bonds, they allow the hair to stretch slightly, while the stronger but less numerous disulphide bonds resist the movement. To obtain greater extension, the stretching is carried out on wet hair, by either winding tightly on rollers or by brushing when blow-drying. Figure 5.1a shows dry hair in its unstretched state, with a hydrogen bond between the hydrogen and oxygen atoms. When wet hair is stretched (Figure 5.1b) water molecules enter the hydrogen bonds allowing the hair to stretch further – this is known as 'bound water'. During drying, the bound water is evaporated off. In Figure 5.1c you can see that because the water is evaporated off while the hair is still in its stretched state, the bonds have reformed in different positions. When the rollers, or brush, are removed, the hair remains in its stretched state. It will not return to its normal state until the hair is wet, but because hair is hygroscopic (it absorbs moisture from the atmosphere – generally about 10 per cent of the cortex can be water) the cohesive set will be lost quickly unless it is protected from moisture. We protect it with various setting agents such as setting and blow-dry lotions, hairsprays, etc. If it were not protected the sequence shown in Figure 5.1 would be reversed and the set would be lost.

What are the two types of keratin involved in a cohesive set?

You may have heard people talking about two types of keratin as if they were totally different things. These are alpha-keratin and beta-keratin. Put simply, alpha-keratin is keratin in its unstretched state, while beta-keratin is keratin in its stretched state. It is rather like alpha-keratin being an unstretched spring, while beta-keratin is the stretched spring. Remember that it is the spring-like structure of the cortex that gives hair its elasticity. Set hair is hair which has been dried in a stretched state, so it is beta-keratin. If it is wetted it returns to being alpha-keratin. Remember that there are still powerful disulphide bonds intact in the cortex which will help pull the hair back to its original shape once the new hydrogen bonds are broken by absorbed water. The two types of keratin are summarised in Figure 5.2.

Figure 5.2 Alpha-keratin and beta-keratin

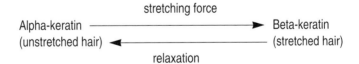

Is there a difference between the cohesive set and the heat-setting carried out on dry hair with heated tongs?

The simple answer to this question is yes. The use of heated waving irons, tongs, crimpers, rollers, etc. is often thought by hairdressers to work in exactly the same way. Hair is both heated and stretched at the same time and then held under tension until it is cool. The hydrogen bonds between the polypeptide chains of keratin are broken by both the heat and the tension placed on the hair. The greater the heat applied, the more bonds will be broken. The hair takes up the shape of the tool used. As the hair cools under tension, the hydrogen and oxygen atoms of the original bonds are too far apart to reform, so they form new bonds with atoms close by which keep the hair in its new shape. Cold water has little effect on a heat set; hot water must be used to break the new bonds so that the hair can relax its structure and reform the original bonds. Remember that too much heat-setting will damage the cuticle of the hair.

Finger waving

Finger waving is the art of shaping hair into waves using a comb and the fingers. It is best carried out on wet hair which has had a setting aid applied because the hair can be controlled a lot more easily. Hair which has been taper cut (see Chapter 4) is much easier to finger wave than club (blunt) cut hair. Before rollers were introduced to Britain from the United States, all sets were done using a combination of finger waves and pincurls. It was around this time that long metal clips were also introduced to help form and hold finger waves. These looked very similar to the 'butterfly' clips in use today for sectioning but the metal ones were longer. Although these clips do not produce such a beautiful result as when the hair is waved with the fingers, several hairdressers who have been been bequeathed these clips from grandmothers think they should be relaunched.

If you watch old movies on television you will notice the finger waves of the stars like Jean Harlow. However, this skill is fundamental to many styles and you will see waved hair in the top fashion magazines. The variations of the styles may change but the method of creating them still requires great skill.

Looking at a diagram of a wave (Figure 5.3) you will see that it is made up of crests and troughs. The crest is the raised part of the wave and the trough is the dip or hollow between two crests. Technically speaking to be called a wave, there must be two crests and one trough. The distance between two crests should ideally be about 3 cm and this space is called the width of the wave. The height of the crest and the depth of the wave is determined by the way in which the hair is directed during combing. The S-shaped movements created by finger waving can look stunning. For those training in hairdressing it teaches the skills of controlling and directing hair. It also demands discipline and manipulative skills to become practised. The hair is moulded and shaped into waves to the form of the head and in the direction of the natural hair growth patterns. The waves encircle the head and can be formed with a parting (side or centre) or straight back from the face without a parting.

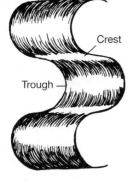

Figure 5.3 A wave showing the crests and troughs

The best type of comb to use for waving is a straight comb with wide-spaced and narrow-spaced teeth. The way the comb is held is important because it will help you to have maximum control over the hair. The comb should be held with the thumb and little finger on one side, with three fingers on the other. This may seem strange to you at first if you are not used to holding a comb in this way, but with practice it will seem like an extension

Figure 5.4 How to hold a comb for finger waving

of your hand. The method of holding of a comb for finger waving is shown in Figure 5. 4 .

Guidelines for finger waving

- Keep your forearm up level with your hand when finger waving to give you maximum control.
- Always stand immediately behind the portion of the head you are waving.
- Hold the comb as shown in Figure 5.4.
- Keep the hair wet.
- Apply a setting aid to the hair.
- The hair should be combed away from the face before waving to look for the natural hair growth patterns.
- Use only the index finger and second finger during waving.

Finger waving practice

Like many hairdressing skills it is often best to practise on a tuition head (otherwise known as a block or 'dummy' head) before progressing to a live model. Before you attempt to wave a whole head, practise the following exercise:

Figure 5.5 Directing the hair in preparation for a finger wave

1 If using a hair weft, secure this to a malleable block using postiche pins. If using a tuition head, make a parting across the back of the head from ear to ear just below the crown area and secure the front hair out of the way. Thoroughly comb the hair, wet it and apply a setting aid such as gel.
2 Begin by combing the hair in a semicircular movement which will direct the hair to the right. Remember that you should be standing immediately behind the portion of the head you are waving and keep your forearm up level with your hand. Place your index finger (of the hand not holding the comb) firmly against the head about 3 cm below the top of the weft or parting that you have made, to hold the curve you have just made in position as in Figure 5.5. Keep your finger firmly in position so that you are able to comb the rest of the hair without the curve being disturbed.
3 To form the crest (raised part) of the wave insert your comb about 2 cm below your index finger, and holding the comb flat against the head, push the comb up towards your finger in a movement directed to the left. Do not remove your comb from the hair at this stage. Move your hand position so that your second finger is resting on the teeth of your comb. Carefully slip out your comb so that you are able to hold the crest between your two fingers by pressure either side of the crest. Try not to pinch the crest too much or it will be distorted. While your fingers hold the crest in position, you can continue this sequence of movements down the rest of the hair.
4 The second crest can now be following the same series of movements but this time the hair is directed in the opposite direction. This is shown in Figure 5 6 .
5 This series of movements continues all the way down the head and, to finish, the hair is pincurled using flat barrel curls. The pincurls are formed so that they continue the wave movement and are wound up to sit just below the final wave crest.

Figure 5.6 Holding the first crest in position while making the second crest to form a complete wave movement

Finger waving a whole head

1 After the hair has been shampooed find the natural direction and fall of the hair so that you can see where the first wave should be placed. Apply a setting aid to the hair.

2 Combing the hair in its natural direction is the start of your first wave. Place your index finger below the crest you have just formed and your second finger above it. You can increase the height of this crest if you wish by inserting your comb at the root area and slightly lifting it upwards.

3 You should be able now to release your hold on the crest and it will remain in position. Following the same movement that you have just done, you are ready to wave the hair to the side of your first wave. Allow only your two fingers to touch the head so that you do not disturb your first crest.

4 Continue your waving around the head in the same direction so that you finish on the other side of the head at the hairline. You can then start to form your next crest right round the head. At the crown area the crest of the wave should be slightly faded to make it look more natural. This is called 'losing a wave' and is done by slightly flattening the crest.

5 It is important that you check the waves are equally balanced on both sides of the head if you decide to wave both sides of the head first and then join them up at the back.

6 When you have finished the waving the points of the hair at the nape and sides can be pincurled to the last crest. Try to avoid using clips to hold the waves in place for drying as these will leave marks on the hair. Instead, use tape positioned in the trough part of the waves.

7 When dry, the hair is combed through by retracing the movements of the waves and the pincurls dressed into curls or waves. Smoothing a little dressing cream through the hair before dressing the waves will give you better control if the hair is flyaway and make the hair shine. The result is shown in Figure 5.7.

Figure 5.7 A finger-waved head

Pincurling

Pincurling is the sculpting of wet hair into a series of wound coils to form a curl. Once the curl is formed, it is secured in place with fine pins or clips. There are many types of pincurl, each producing a different effect, but they fall into two main categories: flat pincurls and stand-up pincurls.

Flat pincurls

As the name implies, this type of pincurl is formed and then positioned so that it lies flat to the head. It does not therefore produce volume at the roots. Flat pincurls are secured either by fine pins or clips as shown in Figure 5.8. Fine pins will not mark the hair or distort the body of the pincurl and are recommended for securing hair that will mark easily as

in the case of bleached hair and when setting good quality wigs. You will notice that two pins are needed and that they cross each other in the centre.

All pincurls take their direction from the roots and the stem of the pincurl so they are placed in the direction of the finished style. Just like when you put in a roller, your pincurls should be formed and positioned in the way you want the hair to lie in the final dressing. That means directing flat pincurls to the left or the right and stand-up pincurls under or over. The roots of pincurls should always be thoroughly combed so that they are not distorted. Pins or clips must be carefully placed so that the body of the pincurl is not disturbed. The points of the hair must be cleanly enclosed in the pincurl to prevent buckled and distorted ends. If you look at Figure 5.9 you will be able to see the labelled part of a flat, open pincurl. Can you say which direction the hair will lie when it is dressed?

There are four different types of flat pincurls and the hairdresser needs to choose the appropriate technique according to the result that is required. The four different types of flat pincurls are:

- open (barrelspring) pincurls
- closed (clockspring) pincurls
- reverse pincurls
- long stem pincurls.

Figure 5.8 Securing flat pincurls with a clip or fine pins

Figure 5.9 The parts of a flat, even pincurl

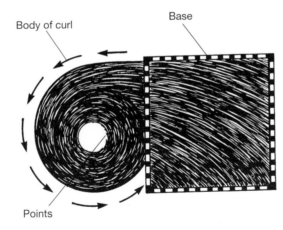

Body of curl

Base

Points

All you need to have clear in your mind at this stage is that all of them are flat pincurls, so they are positioned close to the head, thus creating little or no volume at the roots.

Open (barrelspring) pincurls

These have an open centre and are sometimes referred to as barrelspring or barrel pincurls because they resemble the shape of the spring used in hand hair clippers. This type of pincurl is formed so that as each coil is made it is the same size as the previous one. The points of the hair are neatly enclosed with the coiled hair and should not stick out as this will cause them to be straight or distorted when the hair is dressed.

Figure 5.10 Open or barrelspring pincurl showing the uniform curl pattern that is produced

Figure 5.11 Closed or clockspring pincurl

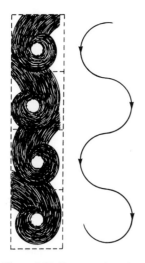

Figure 5.12 Reverse pincurls showing how rows of flat, open pincurls can be used to produce a wave pattern

Because each coil of hair is of uniform size, the result is an even curl formation which can be seen in Figure 5.10. The smaller the loops are made the tighter the end result will be. On short hair, when it might be possible to make only one loop, the result will be a gentle curve in the direction the pincurl was made at the roots, i.e. clockwise (to the left) or anticlockwise (to the right).

Really good results can be achieved when long hair is set using flat, open pincurls because it produces a similar effect to that of rollers but without the volume at the roots.

Closed (clockspring) pincurls

These are called clockspring pincurls because they resemble the shape of the spring found in watches and clocks. You can see from Figure 5.11 that the centre of the pincurl is closed. They produce a more springy curl which is tightest at the points of the hair because each coil is formed around the previous one, which is smaller. Because forming this type of pincurl can begin only at the points of the hair, care must be taken that ends are not distorted and buckled. Closed pincurls are better to use than the open type on hair that drops easily and for tight curls at the nape.

Reverse pincurls

Reverse pincurls are open, flat pincurls arranged so that they produce an S-shaped wave movement when they are dressed. The pincurls are formed so that they are in rows, and directed clockwise and anticlockwise in each alternate row. It is this change of stem direction that produces the wave movement. If you think back to the section on finger waving you will remember that the hair is directed first one way and then the other to form a wave. In reverse pincurling it is the arrangement of the pincurls that create the S-movement. The placement of reverse pincurls is shown in Figure 5.12 along with the dressed result.

Reverse pincurls are dressed in the same way as finger waves. Closed pincurls are not suitable for creating waves because the movement they produce is not uniform and the hair points are too tight to dress into waves successfully.

Long stem pincurls

Long stem pincurls have a long stem which results in straight or slightly curved roots with curl on the ends (see Figure 5.13). The stem of the pincurl creates no volume at all so is often used on fringes and hairline when soft movement is required. Remember that all pincurls take their direction from their stem. This means that long stem pincurls can be formed to create a movement which is slightly curved at the roots to come onto the face or away from it. Alternatively, if you use them on a fringe, you may want the stems to be straight so that the body of the pincurl is responsible for any movement that is produced.

Stand-up pincurls

Stand-up pincurls are always open in the centre and unlike the flat pincurls, create lift and volume at the roots. This volume is produced because a stand-up pincurl actually sits up on the head like a roller. This can be seen in Figure 5.14. Just as the diameter of a roller determines the amount

Figure 5.13 Long stem pincurl

Figure 5.14 Stand-up pincurl

of curl that is put into the hair, the diameter of the open centre of a stand-up pincurl also does the same. Stand-up pincurls can be successfully used to create the same results as rollers because they will create volume at the roots. Like all other pincurls, they take their direction from the stem. The body of the curl may often need support to stop it from distorting or collapsing. Small pieces of cotton wool or crêpe hair are slipped through the open centre which will keep the body of the curl from becoming mis-shapen. To secure a stand-up pincurl, only a clip can be used rather than a choice of fine pins or clips. This is because the clip is slipped through the centre of the curl and holds it in place at the base. They are secured at the base so that the body of the curl is not marked or distorted by the clip. Stand-up pincurls can be formed to produce either a curl movement that turns under or one which flicks upwards just as you can with rollers.

Methods of pincurling

Now that you are aware of the different types of pincurls and the effects that each produces, you need to know how a pincurl is actually formed and the rules governing the shape and size of bases that are used.

Pincurl bases

The base is the foundation of a pincurl. It is the area of the head from which the hair mesh has been taken to form the pincurl and in most cases, where the pincurl will be secured. Three different types of bases for pincurls most commonly used are shown in Figure 5.15.

Figure 5.15 (a) Square base (b) oblong base (c) triangular base

(a)

(b)

(c)

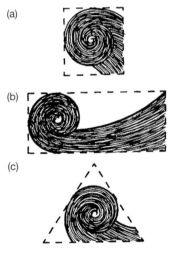

Square base

This shape is probably the one that is used most. This is not because it is the best, but many hairdressers are unaware that other shapes of base can be used that would, in fact, improve their pincurl results.

Oblong base

This shape is used along the front sides of the hairline and allows for the placement of long stem pincurls that are directed away from the face.

Figure 5.16 Oblong bases used with open, long stem pincurls at the side of the head

Figure 5.17 Square bases used for reverse pincurling

Figure 5.18 Forming the curl

Figure 5.19 Angle for holding a mesh of hair for a stand-up pincurl

Triangular base

This shape is ideal for using on the hairline because they help to stop obvious breaks in the finished dressing. This is because the shape of the base allows part of the body of each pincurl slightly to overlap the curl next to it.

Matching bases to types of pincurls

Let's look at how these pincurl bases are used in conjunction with the different types of pincurls.

If you wanted to create a movement at the side of the head which went away from the face and was flat, what type of base and pincurl do you think would be needed? Take a look at Figure 5.16 and you will be able to see that the pincurl bases are oblong allowing the long stem pincurls to sit correctly.

Square bases are best for reverse pincurls because pincurls do not usually have a long stem that needs accommodating, as shown in Figure 5.17.

Triangular bases are best for the top front hairline because they help to prevent splits in the final dressing.

Forming a pincurl

There are two basic techniques you can use to form a pincurl. You can begin to form the pincurl either at the points of the hair or, alternatively, near the roots. You will discover which technique suits you best and the particular type of pincurling you are doing. There are no firm rules to this – after all, it is the result that is important. Incidentally, any curling that begins at the points of the hair is called *croquignole winding* while if it begins at the roots it is called *spiral winding*. That means that when we put in rollers we are winding using the croquignole technique because the roller is introduced to the points of the hair.

Croquignole winding technique

1 Prepare the hair by making a cleanly parted base and comb the ribbon of hair thoroughly in the direction of the pincurl stem that you will be forming.
2 Holding the points of the hair securely between the thumb and index finger, use the thumb and index finger of your other hand to wind the hair towards the head as shown in Figure 5.18.
3 As soon as the pincurl is fully wound, it can then be secured. NB If you are doing a stand-up pincurl the hair should be held out from the head as shown in Figure 5.19 so that it sits on its own base when it is secured.

Spiral winding technique

1 Section the hair so that you have a cleanly parted base. Comb the hair thoroughly right through from the roots to the points to free it from tangles and to make it smooth. During this combing you should be positioning the hair in the direction of the pincurl stem. (Remember that a pincurl takes its direction from the roots.)
2 Hold the comb so that it rests in the palm of your hand so that your fingers are free to hold the points of the mesh.
3 Using the index finger of the other hand, begin to wind the ribbon of hair around your finger as in Figure 5.20. You will need to use your thumb to help hold the wrapped hair in place.

Figure 5.20 Winding the strand of hair around the index finger

Figure 5.21 Sliding the curl off the finger

4 When you have wound all the hair, carefully slide the curl off your finger and wind it down to the head as in Figure 5.21 so that it can be secured.

Guidelines for pincurling

1 Use cleanly parted bases that are the correct shape and size for the effect you want to achieve.
2 Make sure the hair is wet because it will be easier to control and the finished effect will last longer.
3 Thoroughly comb the ribbon of hair from roots to points.
4 Remember that all pincurls take their direction from their stem.
5 Make sure that the points of the hair are neatly enclosed within the pincurl to prevent distorted or buckled ends.
6 Secure the pincurl carefully so that the clip or pins do not cause the body or stem of the curl to be misshapen or marked.
7 Use cotton wool or crêpe hair to pad and support stand-up pincurls that could collapse and distort during drying.

Roller setting

Roller setting is the term used to describe wrapping meshes of hair around cylindrical or conical rollers to produce varying degrees of volume, curl and wave.

Unfortunately, there are far too many hairdressers who think there is only one way to put in a roller – with the roller sitting squarely on a base that is the same size as the roller being used. This is not so! You only have to witness the work of the great competition stylists to see beautiful roller placement that is imaginative and incorporates some of the techniques that will be described. If you can master these techniques you will be able to create varied degrees of volume and movement in hair that will require the minimum of work when you dress it out. Do not fall into the trap of being one of those lazy hairdressers who puts in rollers without giving any thought to the finished look. They are the hairdressers who struggle during the dressing using far too much backcombing and hairspray in an attempt to force the hair in a direction contrary to the way it was set. They have clients with hair that looks shapeless and is difficult for the client to handle because the setting faults have been disguised by the backcombing and hairspray.

There are three considerations to be taken when using rollers and these are:

- degree of movement required (roller size)
- amount of volume required (base size and roller placement)
- direction of the intended style (roller direction).

Degree of movement required (roller size)

There are several factors to consider when deciding which size rollers to use. First, you will need to think about how much movement you want to see in the hair when it is dressed. A mesh of hair wrapped around a roller six times will produce a tighter curl than if it were wrapped three times around a larger roller. The larger the roller, the fewer times the hair can be wrapped around it resulting in looser movements. You will also need to consider the type of hair you are styling. Is it fine and lank, being susceptible to dropping quickly, or has it been permed too tightly for the look the client is hoping for? Is the client looking for a smooth result or something which is tightly curled? Perhaps it is the right time to mention that you should not ask clients what size rollers they think should be put in their hair! This is most unprofessional and signals that you lack the confidence or skill to make this decision yourself. After all, do dentists ever ask you which teeth you would like to be filled? If they did ask you, you would not have much confidence in their ability!

If you are unsure of how the hair will respond to setting and you cannot decide between two roller sizes, it is always advisable to use the slightly smaller ones because you can correct an over-tight set more easily than one which is too loose, which will be described in 'fault-correcting techniques' (Table 5.1, p. 112).

Amount of volume required (base size and roller placement)

As for pincurling, there are different types of bases that are used when using rollers to set the hair. The size and shape of the base and the position that the roller sits on it will determine how much volume there will be in the dressing by the way the roots have been positioned. If you do not want volume at the roots why put it there in the first place? Doing this means having to work harder getting rid of the unwanted volume when you dress out the hair. Alternatively, not enough volume means you have to resort to copious amounts of backcombing to achieve the necessary lift. Read on, and you will discover the technical art of placing rollers that will never have you fighting with hair during dressing again. By the way, your clients will notice the difference too, because their hair will be so much easier to manage and the set will last longer.

A base for roller setting is the area of the scalp where the roller will be positioned and secured – just as for pincurling. Sometimes the bases you use will correspond exactly to the size of the roller you are using. For other techniques the base will be up to twice the diameter of the roller, but will still be as long as the length of the roller. Finally, you will use bases which are not rectangular but shaped like pie-segments.

On-base roller placement

This is the most widely used rollering technique – but not, unfortunately, for the right reasons. There are a large number of hairdressers who think that this is the *only* way of putting in a roller.

As the name implies, the roller is positioned and secured so that it sits exactly on its own base. This produces volume at the roots which depends on the diameter of the roller used. A large roller will produce more volume at the roots than a smaller one because the hair is lifted away from the head much higher. However, if a large roller is used, the curl in the hair will be loose, which is not always what you want.

To put a roller on-base, a base is made which is exactly the same length and diameter as the roller being used. The roller sits exactly on this base as shown in Figure 5.22.

Figure 5.22 On-base roller placement

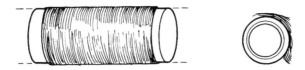

Over-directed roller placement

If you want to achieve maximum volume without necessarily using large rollers the base size you need to use is still the same length as the roller you are using but its width can be up to twice the roller's diameter. The mesh of hair is rolled down so that it sits on the upper part of the base thus creating much more volume at the roots. A diagram of the over-directed roller placement is shown in Figure 5.23a. You will be able to see that the roller is still sitting within the confines of its own base.

Figure 5.23 (a) Over-directed roller placement (b) under-directed roller placement

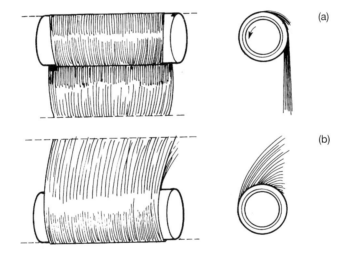

Under-directed roller placement

Sometimes, we want to avoid producing too much volume for certain looks. If you imagine setting a bob, you would not want masses of root lift, but bounce at the ends of the hair. This is an example of when you would use this particular technique. The base is made the same as for an over-directed roller except that the roller is wound down to sit on the lower part of its base. Again you will be able to see that the roller sits within the confines of its own base in Figure 5.23b.

NB If you use this technique on a hairline the roller will actually sit on client's skin and is sometimes called an 'off-base' roller. This is quite acceptable providing it does not cause discomfort to the client.

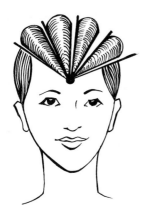

Figure 5.24 Conical rollers placed on pie-shaped bases to create a semicircular movement

Curvature hairstyling using circular roller placement

Curvature hairstyling is based on the fact that the hairdresser is dealing with a rounded object (the head), so all partings and sectioning are in a curved form to blend with the curvature of the head. The type of roller placement uses segment-shaped bases, like pieces of pie; conical rollers are used as opposed to the cylindrical type. This roller placement works on the principle that all the bases are made from the same point so is often referred to as 'pivot' setting. It is used to create circular and semicircular movements in the hair that are impossible to achieve using rectangular bases. The point from which the bases are taken (the pivot) enables the hair to be set so that it fans outwards in a curved movement. An example of using this technique on a hairline is shown in Figure 5.24 .

Direction of the intended style (roller direction)

Apart from being able to control how curly to make the hair and the degree of volume that is introduced, the hairdresser also has the ability to control the direction of the movement in the finished style. This is controlled by the way in which the rollers are positioned in the hair. An example of this is the technique of placing rollers in a circular direction as described above. Also, we sometimes want to produce an upwards flick as opposed to the hair being wound under. The way in which rollers are positioned and combined with pincurls and waves requires practice to create styles which have interest and appeal.

This does not mean that you must place the rollers in brick formation nor that straight rows of rollers are unacceptable. It does mean that *you should place the rollers so that they are in the direction of the finished style.* This might mean putting in rollers in a straight line, or placing them so that they are sitting vertically, or on an angle as opposed to sitting horizontally. It also means *thinking* about what you want the hair to do before you start. This will be more fully explained in the next paragraphs.

Planning a pli

A pli (pronounced as 'plee') is simply the term used to describe a set. People talk about 'first pli' and 'second pli'. 'First pli' refers to the hair in rollers, pincurls, etc. ready for drying. 'Second pli' refers to when the finished style has been dried and dressed. Incidentally, the word pli comes from the French term used for setting which is '*mise-en-pli*' and literally translated this means to 'put into set'.

A good pli does not just happen. Hairdressers must look at the type of hair they are working with, the client's facial and head shape characteristics and also the occasion for which the client is having it done. The natural fall of the hair must be assessed so that the style is not forced against the direction in which the hair grows. Obviously, a lot of this analysis will be done before the hair is even wetted but the hairdresser should look at the hair again once it is wet. After hair has been wetted, the natural movement and direction of the hair can be seen more easily. The hairdresser does this by combing the hair and carefully watching for the way it moves and responds to being combed in different directions. Once

Figure 5.25 A carefully planned pli

the most suitable style directions have been established (in consultation with the client) the stylist can mould the hair. Moulding is combing the hair into the shape, form and direction of the finished look. It is also very helpful to the hairdresser because it identifies areas that will need volume and those that will require movement. By seeing this, it makes the task of deciding which setting techniques to use a lot easier. For example, if the client wants her hair to be very flat at the sides in an upwards movement away from the face, it would be pointless putting in on-base rollers in this area because volume would be created. To achieve this effect, the stylist would find it far better to use flat pincurls as shown earlier. After drying the hairdresser would have a minimum of work to do when dressing out than if rollers had been used.

Figure 5.25 shows an example of a pli which has been carefully planned and will create a style that has movement, shape, volume and indentation.

Styling hair for the individual

The ultimate test of a hairstyle is how well it suits the client. Hairdressers should aim to achieve perfect balance by dressing the hair to compliment the client's characteristics. That means styling the hair to suit the face shape, lifestyle, stature and age of the client and the occasion for which the hair has been styled. Regular clients may request something different from their usual style if they are going to a special function like a ball or party. You may be asked to style a bride's hair for her wedding which may also involve the fitting of her headdress.

Roller practice

To be able to use the techniques described earlier you will need to practise putting in rollers in a variety of ways on all types of hair. Learning roller placement on only one type of hair (like a block) is all right at first, but you must progress to working on different types of hair to appreciate how they respond and behave when dealt with in the same way. Just as a tailor handles certain fabrics in different ways, you as a hairdresser need to learn to handle hair. This experience and skill can only be learnt 'hands on', by actually doing it and feeling the differences yourself.

Whatever size of roller or placement technique is used, there are some fundamental rules about the way you put rollers in. Needless to say, how a roller is put in will determine how the hair will look when the roller is taken out after drying. Do not be misled into thinking that a poorly put in roller will not make any difference to the finished style, or how easy it will be for you to dress. Nothing miraculous happens when the client is under the drier to change bad setting into good setting. What you put into the hair before the client goes under the drier is exactly what you'll get when the hair is dry.

Guidelines for putting in rollers

1 Mould the wet hair into the shape of the style to help you determine your pli.

2 Use only cleanly parted bases which are the correct size and shape for the technique you are using.
3 Place rollers in the direction of the finished style.
4 Ensure the points of the hair are cleanly and smoothly wrapped around the roller to prevent buckled ends.
5 Make sure that the hair is wrapped around the roller with sufficient, even tension.
6 Do not allow the hair to be bunched on the roller but evenly distributed and smooth.
7 Secure the rollers firmly, but do not cause discomfort to the client or cause marks on the hair by poor placing of the pins.
8 If you are not completely satisfied with your pli, make the changes before the client goes under the drier.

Drying the hair

Once the hair is in pli, you will need to place your client under a hood drier so that the hair can be dried. Depending on the type of drier you have in your salon, you may need to put a hairnet over the rollers to prevent the hair being disturbed by the airflow of the drier. If you do need to use a net, check that it does not interfere with your pli by pushing down onto pincurls, etc. You will need to place some form of protection over the client's ears to stop the heat from making them too hot. Any form of ear protection used should ideally be disposable to avoid the transfer of germs. Pads of cotton wool are ideal for this purpose. When you place the client under the drier there are a number of things you should do:

- Make sure there are no pins or clips placed so that, once heated, they could burn the client's skin.
- You should be able to estimate the approximate drying time so that you can tell the client. It is not unknown for the hairdresser to forget about someone under the drier.
- Check that the drier you intend to use is in good working order and safe to use.
- Ensure that your client is comfortable and that the hood is correctly positioned so that all the hair will be dried.
- Explain to clients how to control the heat themselves if the drier you are using has this facility.
- Ask clients whether they would like tea or coffee and magazines; ash trays should be provided if smoking is allowed in your salon and the client smokes.

Checking that the hair is dry

If the hair is not completely dry when you begin dressing it, you are heading for disaster. The hair has to be only a little bit damp for the style to collapse in a matter of hours. To check that the hair is dry, always remove a roller at the crown and at the back of the head and feel for dampness at the points. Do not try to do this if you have just had your hands in water as you will probably think the hair is dry when in fact it is not, because your hands will be very slightly damp. If you are unsure, there is no harm in asking someone to check it with you – it is always worth a second opinion if you are in doubt. If you find the hair is still damp, replace the roller or pincurl and put the client back underneath the drier until the hair is completely dry.

Removing the rollers

Once you are positive that the hair is dry, you should ideally allow the hair to cool for a couple of minutes before you start removing the rollers and clips. If you remove them when the hair is still hot, the action of removing the rollers could loosen the set. If the hair is long, start taking out the rollers at the nape area first, or the hair could get tangled.

Wrap round

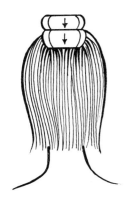

Figure 5.26 Two rollers are placed on the crown using the on-base roller technique

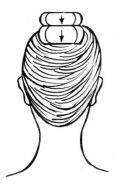

Figure 5.27 The hair is wrapped around the head until it is sleekly stretched

A wrap round is a setting method which can be used to straighten long wavy or curly hair temporarily.

1 Using very large rollers, place two on the crown using the on-base roller technique as in Figure 5.26.
2 Make a side parting and begin wrapping the hair around the head (the head acts like a large roller). Using a brush often helps the stylist to have greater control of the hair during wrapping and puts more tension on the hair, helping it to be stretched out more easily.
3 The wrapping of the hair around the head continues until the head looks like Figure 5.27, with all the hair sleekly stretched around the head. If possible, try not to use any clips on the hair to keep it in place as these will mark the hair, causing indentations on it. Instead, keep the hair wet and use a setting aid to bind the hair together.
4 The hair is protected by a setting net and dried under a hood drier, making sure that the net does not mark or disturb the wrapped hair when it is tied.
5 Halfway through the drying time, some stylists re-wrap the hair in the opposite direction to prevent the roots from taking on one direction. This is a difficult procedure because the hair is semi-dry and tricky to control. This re-wrapping can be omitted.
6 When the hair is dry, the rollers are removed and the wrap is undone and brushed. Because the hair will have dried to the direction in which it was wrapped, the stylist will now need to style the hair by blow drying it with a brush and hair drier. The hair is not redamped, and small sections are taken to stretch and smooth the hair. When all the hair has been blow-dried, the ends may require the use of tongs or a hot brush to achieve bend and body.

Molton Browners

Molton Browners are an alternative to using traditional setting rollers. They are not rigid, being made from cotton-covered wire and foam which is bent to hold in position, so do not require pins or clips. They can be used in a variety of ways to achieve tight curls, gentle waves on long hair, or bounce and body on shorter hair. Even waist-length hair can be set on Molton Browners; this would be extremely tricky and time-consuming if conventional rollers were used.

Molton Browners should be used on clean, *dry* hair. The small amount of heat lost through the head is sufficient to aid the setting of dry hair. Additional heat from a hairdrier can also be used to speed up the process. Molton Browners come in two sizes: pink which are half an inch (1.25 cm) in diameter and red which are one inch (2.5 cm) in diameter.

Creating deep waves in long hair

Use large sections of hair and the pink Molton Browners. First, twist the mesh of hair fairly tightly and then roll the twisted hair up along the Molton Browner. The Molton Browner is held in position by simply bending it in half, as can be seen in Figure 5.28. A styling aid is sometimes applied to the hair (usually by spraying) at this point, but it can wet the hair too much as it will take a long time to dry while twisted. In the salon it is normal practice to put the head under a drier for between 10 and 15 minutes to help the hair take on the shape of the Molton Browners. The finished result can be seen in Figure 5.29.

Figure 5.28 Molton Browners are bent over to secure them in place on the head; the twisted hair can clearly be seen on the Molton Browners (Courtesy Molton Brown)

Figure 5.29 Deep waves created by using Molton Browners (Courtesy Molton Brown)

Creating tight curls on long hair

The technique is exactly the same as before except that the sections need to be smaller. The completed set can be seen in Figure 5.30, and the finished result can be seen in Figure 5.31.

Figure 5.30 Molton Browners wound to produce tight curls on long hair (Courtesy Molton Brown)

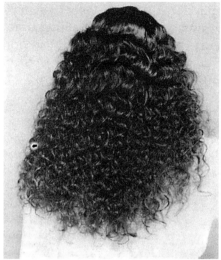

Figure 5.31 The finished result is a mass of tight curls (Courtesy Molton Brown)

For open, bubbly curls, do not twist the hair before rolling up. For setting medium length, layered and short hair, use the red Molton Browners, rolling the hair without twisting it first. By bending the sides of the Molton Browner forward the hair will be held in place.

Dressing-out the pli

Brushing the hair

Do not be afraid to brush the hair after setting – the set will not come out that quickly. You should brush the hair in the direction that the pli was made (i.e. the direction that the hair will be in the finished look) using a flat brush which has nylon or natural bristle filaments. The purpose of this brushing is to blend the hair and get rid of the partings caused by the rollers and also to get the stiffness out of the hair which the setting aid gives it. When you are brushing the hair at this stage, you should be moulding it into the desired shape. You will be able to see the areas that will require backcombing, to give the necessary support and fullness. Do remember that if your pli was well planned, the amount of work you will now need to do will be minimal, and you should not automatically backcomb the hair as it may not need it. You will probably see some hairdressers do this out of habit, but it is not always necessary.

Dressing the hair

If the hair you are dressing does require some support in the way of back-combing or backbrushing, bear in mind that no matter how much of this you put into the hair, there should be no trace of it showing in the finished dressing. Nothing looks more ugly than knotted hair showing through a finished style. If backcombing and backbrushing are done properly in the first place, you should be able to dress the hair so that it looks clean and polished without it showing.

Backcombing

As the name implies this is using the comb to make the hair go back on itself to provide support, height and volume. However, it is often used to disguise a poor pli by redirecting hair into the desired position. Backcombing should always be done in the direction that you want the hair to go and this is often called 'directional backcombing'. The most important factor about backcombing is the size of mesh that you take. It should not be wider than the part of the comb you will be using. For example, if you back-comb using half of the teeth in the comb only, and you take meshes which are wider, it results in some of the hair being missed. Also, you should use only meshes which are slightly deeper than the length of the teeth of your comb. Too deep a mesh will mean that some of the hair will be missed by the teeth, while if the meshes are too narrow, the backcombing will show through the front of the mesh and be difficult to clean out.

When you backcomb, the shorter hairs within the mesh are pushed down towards the roots, providing a supportive padding to the mesh of hair. The comb you use to backcomb should have both close and widely set teeth, but it is the fine teeth that are used to put in the backcombing. Holding the mesh of hair in the direction of the finished style, and at a 90 degree angle to the part of the head you are working on, your comb should be inserted about two-thirds of the way down its length. It is then pushed down to the roots to take the shorter hairs with it as shown in Figure 5.32. Notice that it is the *underside* of the mesh that is backcombed, so that it does not show when the hair is dressed. Because backcombing should always be done in the direction of the style, you will need to change your position around the client, to be standing directly behind the part of the head you are dealing with at any time. This action is repeated until the required degree of support is achieved but do remember that, by pushing some of the hair down to the roots, the amount of hair at the points will be reduced.

Backcombing should be carried out in a systematic fashion so that areas requiring the support are not missed. After the backcombing has been put in, the hair is dressed using the widely spaced teeth of your comb. This end of the comb is used because the narrow teeth would clean out the backcombing you have worked so hard at putting in. The mesh of hair is gently combed into position ensuring that the support and volume of the backcombing is not removed. When the hair is in position, you should not be able to see any trace of backcombing.

Figure 5.32 Backcombing a mesh of hair

Figure 5.33 Backbrushing requires the brush to move in a turning movememt

Backbrushing

Backbrushing is similar to backcombing because although done with a brush, it does increase the apparent volume of the hair. Again it is the shorter hairs on the head that are responsible for adding the support and volume, but backbrushing does not produce as much 'stiffness' to the hair because it does not reach the roots of the hair as backcombing does. However, it is really effective for hair that needs dressing into voluminous curls because it makes the hair separate and increase in width. The brush is used in a turning action so that the filaments of the brush nearest to the client's head meet the hair first with the rest of the brush following. The brush filaments furthest away from your client's head will be the last to have contact with the mesh of hair. If you are doing it properly your wrist will ache! As with backcombing, you need to hold the mesh of hair you are doing firmly between your fingers away from the other hair. This is shown in Figure 5.33.

Checking the balance of the dressing

When you are actually dressing the hair, you should always be aware of the shape and form you are creating by looking at frequent intervals in the mirror in front of the client. You should be checking that the balance of the style is properly proportioned and as you planned it. You should also be checking that the hair is cleanly finished and that there are no hairs sticking out where they should not be. You need to check not only the front view in the mirror but also the profile (side) and back views as well. This might mean that you have occasionally to stand slightly away from your client to see the overall shape. The best styles are those that compliment the natural form of the head as well as the client personally. When you (and your client) are satisfied with the dressing you are ready to apply hairspray, if desired, and show the client the back view of the style. Use a back mirror to display the finished style to the client (see the bottom of the page).

Fault-correcting techniques

It is important that you are able to recognise any mistakes in your work and, once identified, are able to correct them. Such mistakes are usually seen and identified only when the client is taken out from under the drier. Table 5.1 lists the most common faults that occur during setting, together with suggested methods of correction.

Using a back mirror

Clients are able to see their hair from the back if the stylist holds a mirror behind them to reflect an image (which the client would not otherwise see) onto the main styling mirror. When holding a back mirror, try not to move it around too quickly or you will not give the client enough time to see the back properly. Always check that back mirrors are kept clean and free from fingerprints and smears.

With long hair, where it is not possible to show clients all of their hair by this method, turn the client's chair around so that the back is facing the

Table 5.1 Fault-correcting techniques

Problem	Cause	Solution
Buckled ends	Points of hair not wrapped properly when set	As your client will not want you to cut them off, try using a pair of tongs to reshape the ends
Hair not dry	Hair not checked properly	If the hair has not been brushed, replace the client under the drier; otherwise, use a blow-drier on the affected areas in conjunction with a circular brush
Hair too curly	Rollers (or equivalent) too small	Use a blow-drier and hairbrush to stretch and relax the hair
Set too loose	Incorrect size (too big) of rollers, etc.	Use tongs to curl affected areas
Hair going in wrong direction	Incorrect placement of rollers, etc.	Try to redirect hair using either a blow-drier or tongs
Hair is flyaway and difficult to control	Too much shampoo was used or could be the natural characteristic of the hair, especially if it is fine	Apply some dressing cream or spray to the hair
Hair is lank and greasy	Poor shampooing or hair insufficiently rinsed after a conditioner was applied	No alternative other than re-shampooing and setting the hair

styling unit mirror. If clients hold the mirror at a slight angle and look into it, they will be able to see the back of their hair more easily. Clients with very long hair will need to stand up to see it all.

Alternative setting techniques

The use of Molton Browners is an example of setting the hair using equipment other than rollers and pincurl clips. Here are some other setting techniques which can be used by themselves or combined to create the look your client wants.

Chopsticks

Using chopsticks to set the long hair is a spiral method of winding that will produce uniform ringlets which are resilient and perfectly formed.

1 Shampoo and towel-dry hair. Apply a setting lotion and comb through.
2 Divide hair from forehead to nape down the centre.
3 Make a section as shown on Figure 5.34 which is approximately 6 cm (2.5 inches) deep. The remaining hair should be clipped neatly out of the way.

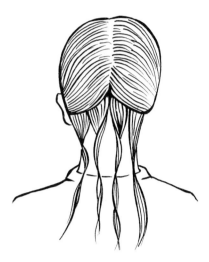

Figure 5.34 Chopstick winding begins at the nape, using sections approximately 6 cm × 4 cm

4 This section is then divided so that meshes of hair approximately 4 cm (1.5 inches) wide are wound on the chopstick.
5 To wind, the chopstick is held in the right hand and the left hand winds the mesh securely round it starting from the root. The points are secured using a pipe cleaner. To prevent the chopstick from slipping, the chopstick is turned a full 360 degrees a couple of times and a setting pin is then pushed through the twisted roots to hold it firmly in position. This twisting at the root also ensures that the roots will have movement. A wound chopstick is shown in Figure 5.35.

Figure 5.35 A wound mesh is secured onto the chopstick

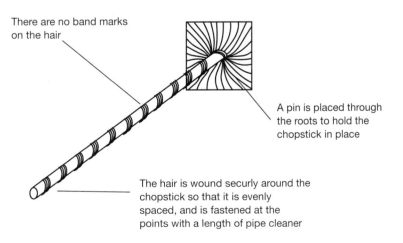

There are no band marks on the hair

A pin is placed through the roots to hold the chopstick in place

The hair is wound securly around the chopstick so that it is evenly spaced, and is fastened at the points with a length of pipe cleaner

6 When the hair is dry, the chopsticks are carefully removed (starting at the bottom and working upwards) and the hair is gently arranged using an Afro comb, a chopstick, or the fingers.

Mad Mats – step by step

Mad Mats can produce a range of effects from tight zig-zags to soft spiral curls. The Mad Mats are manipulated into shape to give the required result. If you want a crimped look, corrugate the Mat; if you want a spiral curl, twist the hair round the full length of the Mat.

1 Long, naturally wavy hair is shampooed and excess moisture is removed to leave the hair damp.
2 The hair is divided so that the back, underneath hair is wound first. A mesh of hair is taken and the Mat is folded in half lengthways, over the hair.

 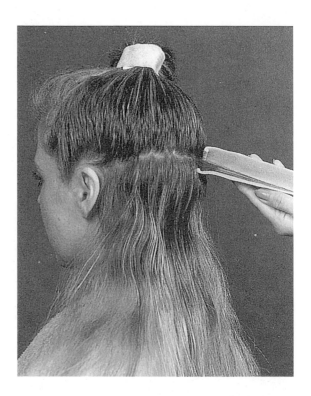

3 The end of the tail comb is used to make a crease at the root which will hold the Mat securely in place.
4 The Mat is bent into a zig-zag using the end of the tail comb. As this hair is very long, a second Mat is joined to the first so that all the hair can be wound.

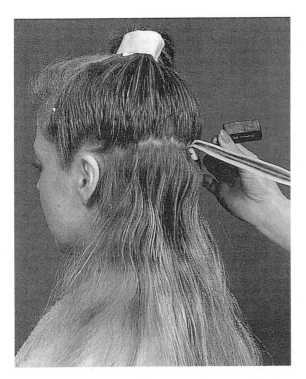 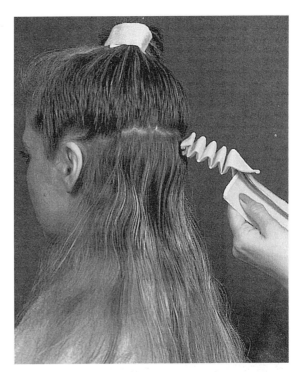

5 Use as many Mats as are needed to wind the length of the mesh, ensuring that the zig-zag is equally proportional. Continue winding the rest of the hair in this way.

6 The completed wind, showing just what an eye-catcher this would be in the salon!

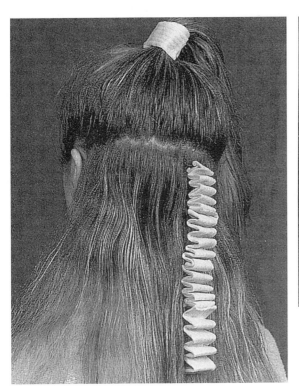 

7 The finished result shows the zig-zag form that has been created in the hair.

(Photographs courtesy of Mad Hackers Hair Asylum)

Note: Similar effects can be produced using aluminium foil instead of Mad Mats.

Rik-Raks

Meshes of hair are wound through the prongs of the Rik-Raks to create deep zig-zag waves and secured at the points using a perm rod.

1 Shampoo and towel-dry hair. Apply a setting lotion and comb through.
2 Starting at the nape, make square sections, no larger than 3 cm (just over an inch).
3 Use an end paper (as used in perming) and wind two to three turns on a small diameter perm rod.
4 Place the mesh of hair between the arms of the Rik-Rak and weave the hair in a figure of eight. See Figure 5.36.
5 Continue taking meshes working towards the crown, then do the sides in the same manner remembering to work up to either side of the parting. Try to place the Rik-Raks in a brick formation so that they rest between one another. This will help to balance the waves evenly and

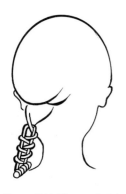

Figure 5.36 Figure of eight

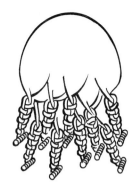

Figure 5.37 Roots are left free

prevent unnatural breaks in the final dressing. The Rik-Rak does not necessarily need to be positioned close to the scalp. For a smooth crown area, the Rik-Raks would be positioned as shown in Figure 5.37.

6 After drying, the Rik-Raks are carefully removed (from the bottom upwards) and the hair is gently arranged using an Afro comb or the fingers.

Revision Questions

1 What does the term 'hygroscopic' mean?

2 Does setting bring about a physical or chemical change to the hair?

3 Why must hair be in good condition to take a set well?

4 Which bonds are affected during a cohesive set?

5 What causes a set to drop or be completely lost?

6 What are the two types of keratin?

7 What effect does finger waving produce?

8 Describe the terms 'crest' and 'trough'.

9 What is the most suitable type of comb to be used for finger waving?

10 How are pincurls secured?

11 What are the two main types of pincurls?

12 Name the four types of flat pincurls.

13 What are croquignole winding and spiral winding?

14 What considerations should be taken into account when choosing the size of rollers?

15 How does roller size affect the amount of volume produced?

16 List three different roller placement techniques and their effect.

17 What does 'first pli' and 'second pli' mean?

18 How do you check that the hair is dry?

19 Why should the hair be allowed to cool before removing the rollers?

20 Where should you begin removing rollers from long hair?

21 On what type of hair would you select the wrap round technique of setting?

22 List at least three alternative methods of setting hair and the effects they create.

23 Make a list of points that are important for successful backcombing.

24 What action would you take if you found the set had caused the hair to be too curly?

25 What action would you take if you found the set had caused the hair to go in the wrong direction?

Advanced Questions

1 With the aid of diagrams, describe the cohesive set.

2 Write guidelines for finger waving hair.

3 With the aid of diagrams, describe the effect achieved by each of the following types of pincurls and an example of when each would be used:

  (i) open and closed flat pincurls

  (ii) reverse pincurls

  (iii) long stem pincurls

  (iv) stand-up pincurls

4 With the aid of diagrams, describe the effect achieved by each of the following roller techniques and an example of when each would be used:

  (i) on-base

  (ii) over-directed

  (iii) under-directed

5 With the aid of diagrams, describe how a wrap round is carried out and dressed.

6 Describe different effects which can be achieved by the use of alternative setting techniques.

Chapter 6

BLOW-DRYING

Introduction

Blow-drying (or blow-styling as it is also known) is a method of drying and shaping the hair using a hand-held drier in combination with brushes, combs or the hands. The hair is stretched, shaped and dried simultaneously, and the tool which is used determines the finished look. During the gradual evaporation of the moisture from the hair while being stretched, the hydrogen bonds reform in different positions, and the hair takes on a new shape as they do during a setting. Therefore, blow-drying is also classified as a cohesive set because the hair undergoes the same physical change as when the hair is wrapped and dried on rollers.

What effects can be achieved by blow-drying?

If the hair is wrapped around a circular brush and dried, the effect produced will be a curl. A mesh of hair dried while it is held straight will be straight. Hair that is 'scrunch-dried' will have movement and texture. Hair that is directed in a particular way and held with a comb during drying will result in a wave. Lift and volume can be achieved by over-directing a mesh of hair and directing the airflow at the roots. Conversely styles that lie close to the head, requiring little or no volume, can be achieved. Blow-drying can also temporarily straighten hair. Smooth, sleek styles can be produced or spiky and 'rough' looks. The finished look can be either casual or sophisticated but there is one fact that is paramount in the success of a blow-dry: hair that is cut well and in good condition will always produce the best results.

Blow-drying techniques and their effects are described in Table 6.1.

How is the most suitable drying technique selected?

The skill of blow-drying is knowing when to use the various drying techniques on different hair types to produce the desired effect. The finished result should also compliment the client's facial characteristics.

Certain hair textures are better for achieving particular looks and effects than others, and selecting an unsuitable drying technique can result in the hairdresser struggling with the hair. Table 6.2 sets out the various drying techniques to help you to select the most suitable method of blow-drying.

Table 6.1 Blow-drying techniques and their effects

Drying technique	Effects
Flat brush	Used to dry sleek styles but can also add bounce (e.g. bob)
Circular brush	Creates curl and movement in the hair – the smaller the brush, the tighter the curl
Vent brush	Creates a natural finish to the hair with a soft, 'broken' effect
Finger-drying	Produces a natural, casual look
Scrunch-drying	Produces a rough finish with curl and movement
Natural drying	Achieves an effect that is totally natural because the hair is allowed to dry (using infra red) with minimum disturbance
Blow-waving	Creates waves in the hair to look like finger waves
Finger-pressing	Creates a sleek finish to smooth straight one-length styles

Table 6.2 Blow-drying techniques and their suitability

Drying technique	Suitability
Flat brush	Curl cannot be achieved with a flat brush although the slight curve of the brush where the filaments are embedded can produce bounce. This brush can also be used to smooth out movement from the hair during drying. Suitable for most hair lengths, especially long hair. This is probably the most frequently used brush in salons today.
Circular brush	Suitable for most hair lengths except very long hair which is not layered. Circular brushes can easily tangle in the hair if the hair is fine and long. The diameter of the brush determines the degree and tightness of the curl. Circular brushes are also good for adding bounce and curl to the points of one-length styles.
Vent brush	The filaments of a vent brush are arranged in pairs and the hair is brushed; the shorter filaments break up the hair so that it lies as if fingers have been drawn through it. Ideal for using on most hair lengths except very long hair which is fine because the filaments can get caught in the hair.
Finger-drying	Suitable for straight, curly or wavy hair if the hair's curl formation is to remain virtually unchanged. This technique is best for fashion looks that require a casual finish.
Scrunch-drying	Not suitable if hair has no wave or curl. Also unsuitable for hair which is very short or long hair that is not layered.
Natural drying	Suitable for clients who want their hair to look natural and casual. Ideal for permed hair and naturally curly hair. Not suitable for clients that like a 'set' look or require a lot of root lift.
Blow-waving	Suitable for short hair if it is not too curly. Mostly used on male clients although it is equally good for female clients. Blow-waving is difficult to do on hair that is sparse and should be in the direction of the natural growth patterns on the front hairline.
Finger-pressing	This technique is used only for styles that are straight. It is used to smooth the surface of the hair so that it is ultra-sleek and shiny.

A few clients are apprehensive about having a blow-dry, instead of their usual shampoo and set. If you are blow-drying an elderly client's hair, try to create soft lines around the face to prevent the style from looking severe. If the client is used to height and curl, blow-dry the hair to produce this effect. The style can always be finished with tongs or a hot brush after it has been dried. Do remember that there are too many hairdressers who suggest styles which are typical 'granny' looks because of the person's age. It is the facial characteristics which should be the main consideration, not the client's age. Just because a client is 70 does not mean she should have a shapeless shampoo and set. A new style which is blow-dried can be more suitable if it is thoughtfully planned to compliment the client.

Principles for blow-drying

- A style will always lie better and last longer if it follows the natural hair fall and movement.
- The hair should be directed to the movement of the intended style, taking its direction from the roots. This can be achieved only if the root area is dried before the middle lengths and ends. Lift at the roots cannot be successfully achieved if the roots are not dried first. To increase the volume at the roots, over-direct the mesh of hair and direct the airflow in at the roots.
- The drier should always be kept moving to prevent damage to the hair or scalp.
- The depth of meshes to be dried should be no deeper than the diameter of the brush being used.
- Wherever you begin drying the hair, it is essential that the mesh is completely dry before going onto another mesh. If you fail to dry a particular area thoroughly, the remaining moisture will evaporate, causing the style to collapse.
- When blow-drying, the airflow should be directed so that it follows the lie of the cuticle (i.e. roots to points) because if the cuticle is kept smooth, the hair will shine.
- You will need to position yourself and the client so that you can get at the hair easily. Sometimes, you may need the client to lean right forward so that you can dry the hair at the nape. This is often done when scrunch-drying to achieve maximum volume and support in the underneath hair.
- During the blow-dry you will need to check the balance and shape of the style by looking in the mirror. You may also find it useful to bend down so that you are at eye level to the client's head when looking in the mirror. This will help you to notice any discord in the shape or balance much more easily.
- Only products intended for blow-drying should be applied. Ordinary setting lotion can dry to be sticky and makes the hair difficult to manage and control. Mousse, gel and other styling aids should be applied to the hair evenly (see Chapter 1). They should be applied to towel-dried hair and thoroughly combed to distribute them evenly throughout the hair. Too much styling product in one area will normally mean there will not be sufficient in another.

- When the blow-dry is finished, check that the hair is completely dry. Comb or brush the hair if necessary, to ensure that the style is blended and looks polished. This is also the opportunity to check that partings are clean and straight.
- The application of hairspray or fixative will help hold the blow style in place, and protect it from atmospheric moisture. If the style you have created is sleek, apply the fixing spray in downward movements to avoid disturbance. Any fine, stray hairs can be gently smoothed down with the hands at this stage, to get the style looking really sleek. Remember that fixing sprays should be applied at a distance of approximately 30 cm and that the client's eyes should be protected during the application. You might also wish to apply finishing products such as gloss sprays, gels or waxes to complete the look. (Remember that this is the ideal time and opportunity for recommending retail products to your client.)
- Always show the client the back of the hair when it is finished by using a back mirror. It should be held so that you are able to see the reflection in the mirror which is in front of the client. Try not to move the mirror too quickly or the client may presume something is wrong with the hair at the back!

How can wastage be minimised?

Blow-drying can be tedious and time-consuming. Time can be saved if excess moisture is removed before styling begins. This can easily be done by towel-drying or rough-drying the hair a little using the drier. Alternatively, the drier can be directed at the roots while the hair is brushed. This will remove excess moisture and at the same time give lift and body to the roots. Only apply as much styling product as the manufacturers recommend. Careful application will prevent any product from ending up on the floor or simply making the towel around the client's shoulders wet. Finally, never waste the opportunity of having your client's undivided attention during a blow-dry, to offer haircare advice and to recommend further services and retail products.

Styling aids

The choice available of styling aids for blow-drying is almost so broad to be confusing. Apart from mousses, blow-drying lotions and gels (see Chapter 1) there has been a huge increase in products designed to 'seal' the hair during blow-drying and help protect it from the heat. Knowing which product to choose relies upon gaining experience of using a range of products and analysing results as well as watching the results achieved by colleagues working alongside you.

Styling aids are applied to hair which is towel dry and should be evenly distributed through the hair. Using too much product will result in over-loading the hair making it difficult to dry and shape. Using too little product will result in the style's durability being reduced. Always read the manufacturer's instructions before using a product. The instructions will tell you how much moisture there should be in the hair (e.g. towel dry), how much to apply, and possibly, the suitability and benefits of the product for different hair types, drying techniques and looks.

Blow-drying a one-length shape

When drying a one-length shape, such as a bob, you will be aiming to produce a sleek look with some bend on the points of the hair. A flat brush is the ideal tool for drying this type of style and the curve of the brush is what you will be using to produce the bend on the hair points.

Blow-drying using a flat brush

1 Prepare hair with styling aid if desired and make any partings that are required.
2 Divide the hair into four sections (forehead to nape and across the top of the head from ear to ear) and secure each division with sectioning clips.
3 Take a section, equivalent to the diameter of the brush you are using, ready for drying. This is shown in Figure 6.1.
4 Working with the hand drier in one hand and the brush in the other hand, place the brush underneath the mesh of hair at the roots. Keeping the tension on the mesh so that it is kept taut (without undue stress), direct the airflow in a downwards movement onto the hair following the downwards movement of the brush. Concentrate on drying the root area first, repeatedly introducing the brush to the roots once it has moved

Figure 6.1 Taking a section as wide as the diameter of the brush you are using

down the length of the hair. Repeat this movement until the hair is dry. Once the roots are dry, use the drier to style the middle lengths and ends, using the curve of the brush to achieve the bend on the hair points.

5 Once the whole of the mesh is dry, take another section of hair (the same depth as the diameter of the brush) above the section you have dried. Dry this section of hair in the same manner as the previous one, ensuring that the root area is dried first. Continue in this manner until all of the back hair is dried.

6 When you have completed the hair at the back, begin at the sides by taking horizontal meshes of hair on the underneath, gradually working upwards towards the parting or top hair. Figure 6.2 shows the final side being dried. Note how the brush is turned in the hand once it reaches the points of the hair, to utilise the curve of the brush, to create the bend on the points. The drier is held so that the airflow is directed downwards, keeping the hair smooth and sleek.

Figure 6.2 The final side of the style being blow-dried: the brush is turned in the hand once it reaches the points of the hair

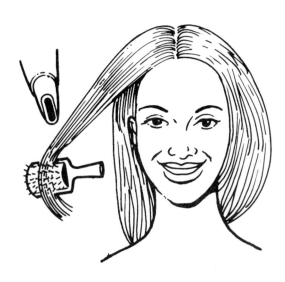

7 To complete the blow-dry the hair can be 'finger-pressed' to achieve optimum smoothness. This is done by taking meshes of the top, overlaying hair between the first two fingers and sliding them down the hair, followed by the airflow. This helps to flatten and smooth the cuticle even more, thereby achieving the maximum degree of shine on the hair.

8 Once the blow-dry is completed, you should always check that the hair is completely dry by feeling it with your hands. When the freshly dried hair is brushed, it should fall into the desired shape. If the ends do not turn under properly and tend to stick out when brushed, check they are thoroughly dry; this will not occur if the hair is completely dry.

Blow-drying using a circular brush

There are many different sizes of circular brushes, varying from about 1 cm in diameter to as much as 5 cm. The smaller the diameter of brush that is used, the greater the amount of movement and curl that will be achieved. It is important to remember that the smaller circular brushes should be carefully used as longer hair has a tendency to tangle with such brushes, especially if the hair is fine.

Large circular brushes can be used to shape one-length hair shapes instead of flat brushes, but the smaller ones are mostly used on shorter lengths when curl is required.

1 Prepare hair with styling aid if desired and comb the hair into its intended direction (that is, make any required parting and comb the hair according to the finished result).
2 If the hair at the nape is long, it is recommended that the drying commences in this area. Otherwise, the drying could begin wherever the stylist prefers. The important thing is that the blow-dry is carried out in a systematic way, using clean partings, correct size meshes, and that each mesh of hair is thoroughly dried before moving onto the next one.
3 It is always important to dry the roots before the middle lengths and ends. Failing to do this will result in the stylist being unable to create any volume at the roots.
4 Dry each mesh of hair and avoid disturbing the movement or curl until it has completely cooled as this will pull out the newly formed shape. When working with a circular brush, make sure that the hair points are cleanly wrapped around the bristles or you could end up with frizzy, distorted ends (that is, fish hooks).
5 On completion of the blow-dry, check that the hair is fully dry and look for any areas that require further styling. Also, check that the style is well balanced in volume and that the hair is falling as intended. You may find it necessary to use tongs or a hot brush to achieve the desired degree of curl or movement, which is an acceptable practice. You should not rely on the tongs or hot brush to produce the style as your blow-drying should have formed the hair into shape.

Blow-drying using a vent brush

If you look at a vent brush, you will notice that the back of the brush has open spaces which allows the airflow from the drier to pass through. Also, the nylon bristles are of two different lengths. It is the venting on the back of the brush and these different length bristles that give the hair a casual, broken appearance when brushed. Therefore, blow-drying with a vent brush is recommended when a textured, casual result is required. Vent brushes can also be used to simply brush through the hair after drying with a flat or circular brush, to break up the hair and create a softer, casual look.

Finger-drying

Sometimes there is no substitute for the fingers to dry the hair into shape. The fingers are used to lift and direct the hair into the intended style, giving a softer and more casual appearance than using a brush. To create lots of volume and texture, as would be seen in spiky styles, place the palm of your hand flat onto the scalp and rotate it in a circular movement, directing the airflow onto this area. The hair will become matted, causing the hair to stand up. Sometimes stylists ask clients to bend their heads forward so that the airflow can be directed underneath the hair at the nape. This helps to increase the body at the roots, making the hair stand out on the supporting hair underneath.

Scrunch-drying

Scrunch-drying is a method of blow-drying using the hands. It helps to increase curl and texture in hair which already has some natural movement. The root area should be dried first, and the clients perhaps asked to bend their heads over to achieve maximum volume first. Then the middle lengths and ends are clasped tightly in the hands while directing heat onto them from the drier. Sections are not normally necessary when drying hair using this technique and quite large quantities of hair can be scrunched as opposed to small meshes. Do not be tempted to brush or comb the hair after scrunch-drying. All your hard work will be lost as brushing would pull out the texture and movement you have created. Many stylists prefer to work with different diffuser attachments when drying hair using the scrunching technique.

Natural drying

There are certain looks that do not require shaping by a brush and hand-held drier. Instead, they are combed or brushed into position and then allowed to dry naturally, perhaps occasionally lifting the hair with the fingers or an Afro comb. Such styles might be those which are permed and require no stretching by blow-drying. Because it would be unreasonable to expect clients to sit in the salon waiting for their hair to dry as they would if they were at home, we use an additional source of heat to accelerate the process.

Perhaps the most popular means of drying hair naturally is by using heat provided from infra red lamps in the form of some sort of accelerator, such as the Wella Climazon, or an octopus lamp. The heat is dry and there is no airflow to disturb the lie of the hair. Care must be taken that the radiation is not directed into the client's face.

If you use a diffuser attachment on a hand hairdrier it will disperse the airflow and will give little disturbance to the lie of the hair. Never allow the client to leave the salon with wet hair as it is possible to catch cold easily as the moisture evaporates.

Relaxing unwanted curl

Using the heat from a drier to aid the relaxation of unwanted curl and movement is used for straightening over-curly hair (e.g. Afro hair) before it is roller tonged and for loosening over-tight sets.

Afro hair which has been chemically relaxed is often dried straight by using a special comb attachment (otherwise called a rake attachment) on the drier. The hair is dried straight by the action of the comb attachment being drawn through the hair from roots to points. Tension must be maintained in order to stretch and smooth the hair so the comb is slightly turned as it is passed through each mesh of hair. Once the hair is dry, it is then roller tonged. It is usually possible to temporarily straighten Afro hair which has not been chemically relaxed (i.e. virgin hair) but the result will not be as smooth as chemically relaxed hair and it will easily revert to its natural curl formation when subjected to atmospheric moisture.

Relaxing over-curly hair

Blow-drying using a brush can be done after the hair has been set on rollers to loosen the hair if it is too curly. The hair is not dampened, as it is the heat from the drier and the tension that you put on the hair that will relax the movement. When doing this, be careful to observe how the hair responds, as it is very easy to over-relax the set, making it limp and lifeless. This technique is most frequently used after doing a wrap round to smooth out the hair.

Blow-waving

The art of blow-waving was developed as a technique during the 1930s using a comb and hand drier to produce waves in the hair, similar to those produced by finger-waving. The comb was traditionally made from vulcanite to withstand heat, as many plastics are softened (though some modern plastic combs are heat-resistant). Blow-waving should start at the front hairline, following the natural hair growth movement and direction. The wide teeth of the comb are used to hold the hair in the wave direction and the airflow is directed onto the hair. Use a low power setting so that the hair does not blow out of position. An important rule of blow-waving is that the airflow is directed along the wave crest against the direction of the movement as shown in Figure 6.3. Use a nozzle attachment to concentrate the airflow of the hairdrier.

Finger pressing

This technique can be used to enhance the shine and sleekness of one-length, smooth styles. Finger pressing is carried out when the hair has

Figure 6.3 The airflow from the hairdrier is directed along the wave crest against the direction of the movement

been completely dried into a sleek style but needs that extra smoothing of the surface hair to improve the finish. Narrow meshes of the surface hair are taken and held firmly between the index and second finger near to the roots. The airflow of the drier is positioned so that it is directed down the length of the hair (following the lie of the cuticle scales) and the fingers and drier slowly move in unison while the fingers are pressing the hair. The naturally shorter hairs present will be inclined to lie flatter and because the cuticle has been further encouraged to lie flat, the hair's shine will improve.

Applying finishing aids

After the blow-dry is finished the client may want hairspray applied. If the style is smooth, direct the spray in a downwards movement to follow the shape of the hair. Then, while the hairspray is still damp, very gently smooth your hand down the hair. This will make any nuisance, shorter hairs which are not lying smooth 'stick' down flat. If the style is not smooth and strands of hair need to be artistically placed, position the hair with the fingers and spray. Any further necessary arrangements of the hair can then be made while the spray is still damp. Apply hairspray at a distance of 30 cm (12 inches) and always use your free hand to protect the client's face, eyes, ears and neck from being sprayed. This protection is especially important if your client is wearing spectacles, contact lenses or jewellery.

Other finishing aids include control creams, brilliantines and sheen sprays (see Chapter 1). These products increase the hair's shine and help reduce static electricity. A little control cream on the fingers can be usefully applied to strands of hair to separate and mould the hair into place. Avoid applying these products too heavily as the hair will become heavy, lank and greasy.

1 Which bonds in the hair are affected during blow-drying?

2 Which blow-drying technique will produce a wave effect?

3 How much moisture should be present for applying styling aids to hair?

4 What size should the meshes be when blow-drying a one-length shape?

5 When blow-drying, why is it important always to dry the roots before the ends?

6 Which drier attachment is often used when scrunch-drying?

7 If the result of a set is too tight, how is it relaxed using a blow-drier?

8 If drying Afro hair straight, what attachment is used on the drier?

9 How is tension on the hair maintained when drying Afro hair straight?

10 In which direction should the airflow be when blow-waving?

11 On which part of the head is blow-waving begun?

12 On what type of style would finger pressing be carried out?

13 Why will the hair's shine improve after finger pressing?

14 What finishing aid should be applied at a distance of 30 cm?

15 How can hairspray be applied to a smooth style to encourage the hair to lie flat?

16 Which finishing aids will improve the hair's shine?

17 Why is it important not to apply too much of the above product?

18 Give an example of when you would naturally dry hair.

19 Make diagrams to show how the following attachments affect the airflow of a hairdrier

   (i) diffuser

   (ii) nozzle

20 Draw and label the parts of a hand-held drier.

1 Make diagrams to show how the following attachments affect the airflow of a hairdrier and give an example of when each would be used:

   (i) diffuser

   (ii) nozzle

   (iii) comb (rake)

2 With the aid of diagrams explain the physical change which takes place to hair during blow-drying.

3 For each of the following products:

   (i) describe how it is applied

   (ii) give an example of its use for different hair types and styles

(iii) describe its effect on the hair

- mousse
- gel
- blow-dry lotion
- hairspray
- brilliantine or oil sheen spray

4   Devise guidelines for blow-drying a one-length shape which includes:

(i) preparation of the hair and application of a styling aid

(ii) sectioning and choice of tools

(iii) drier and brush movements during drying

(iv) health, safety and hygiene considerations

5   Give examples of when each of the following tools would be used:

(i) large circular bristle brush

(ii) small circular brush

(iii) vent brush

(iv) comb

(v) flat brush

Chapter 7

THERMAL STYLING

Introduction

Using heat to reshape hair is not new. Curling irons were used as early as Roman times. Looking back in history, the hair was often curled with irons as were beards and moustaches. Curling irons were made in various sizes and heated in burners and were used to create straight line crimps and curls. It was not until 1872 that a French hairdressser named Marcel Grateau revolutionised the use of hot irons by developing a series of movements which created S-shaped waves with the irons. Hence such irons are often referred to as Marcel irons.

These irons are still used today for theatrical wig styling when re-creating historical hair fashions but they are now heated using electric heaters. Many salons specialising in Afro hair have gone back to using these types of irons, which are now available in a range of sizes for creating soft wave movement or very tight curls. This preference is perhaps due to the range of sizes available, the tighter grip which can be maintained on the hair and the higher temperatures possible. Like pressing combs, Marcel irons operate at between 1.5 and 2.5 times the temperature of boiling water, thus having the heat to break more hydrogen bonds. Pressing combs are used to temporarily straighten Afro hair and have been in existence since the early 1900s. Originally heated only by means of a gas burner, they are now either electrically powered or heated using a special heater, like Marcel irons. Thermal styling is at the forefront of fashion styling in the late 1990s because it is at photographic sessions and fashion shows that hairdressers rely on achieving instant results, quickly. One leading session hairdresser said, 'Give me a comb, a few clips and a pair of tongs, and I can achieve any look the session stylist or designer wants.'

Chemistry of thermal styling

Thermal styling works by breaking down the hydrogen bonds between the polypeptide chains of keratin. Therefore, this causes a physical change to the hair structure. The greater amount of heat used, the more bonds are broken and it is important to remember that these bonds will break more easily if the hair is damaged through the use of chemicals or from physical abuse. The hair is both heated and put under tension (stretched) during thermal styling and takes up the shape of the styling tool used. As the hair cools the atoms of the original bonds will be too far apart to reform their old positions, so will form new bonds with nearby atoms. Water will cause the new bonds to break and the old ones will reform causing a reversal to the natural curl formation.

Tonging techniques

There are as many ways of using tongs as there are techniques to put in rollers. Practise with handling tongs. (i.e. opening and closing them and turning them in your hand) is necessary to become confident in using them. Tongs are made up of a heated rod with a rigid handle and a hollow trough (or groove) that is not heated (see Figure 7.1) The trough has a movable handle (or lever) which enables the tongs to be opened and closed. They should be picked up as though you are about to shake hands with someone and your little finger is used to push the movable handle away from the other one to open them. Some tonging techniques require the tongs to be 'clattered' which means slightly opening and closing the tongs very quickly (while wrapped with a mesh of hair) to allow steam to escape, so it is important that you develop skill in handling them.

Figure 7.1 Parts of tongs

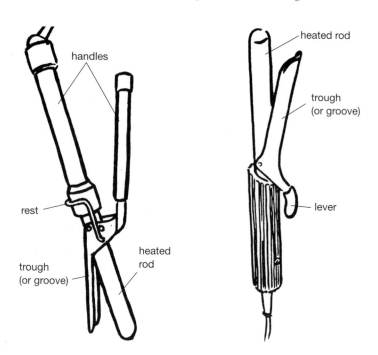

Croquignole

Croquignole is a means of winding the hair starting at the points and working up towards the roots. It is the most commonly used form of winding in hairdressing today. A mesh of hair is taken, cleanly combed so that it is smooth, and then the tongs are closed on the hair (with the trough uppermost) and slid up to the points. (The points must be cleanly wrapped around the rod of the tongs to prevent the ends from becoming buckled.) The tongs are then turned down towards the roots so that hair is evenly wound around the rod. A vulcanite comb, which is more heat resistant than plastic, is placed between the tongs and the scalp to prevent possible burning. Usually ten seconds will be sufficient time for the heat to penetrate the mesh of hair but remember that short hair and chemically treated hair may not require as long. To remove the tongs, they are opened very slightly (by separating the handles with your little finger) to loosen the hair and the curl is gently slid off the rod. Holding the warm curl gently in shape for a few seconds while it cools will prevent it from being disturbed. Figure 7.2 shows the stages of points to roots winding using tongs.

1 A mesh of hair is taken (which is the same size as the rod of the tongs) and combed through. The tongs are inserted into the hair about half way down the mesh and then slid up towards the points.

Figure 7.2 Croquignole technique of tonging hair: the five stages of points to roots winding using tongs

2 The ends are smoothly wrapped around the rod to ensure they are not buckled.

3 The tongs are turned downwards smoothly and evenly.

4 A vulcanite comb is placed at the roots between the tongs and the scalp to prevent steam from the hair or heat from the tongs damaging the scalp.

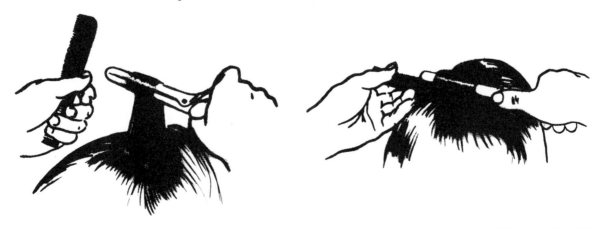

5 The tongs are slightly opened and the curl is slipped off the rod and carefully held in fingers for a few moments while the hair cools.

Roller tonging

After some blow-drying techniques, particularly on Afro hair, the hair will need to be 'roller tonged'. This means using the tongs to create smooth curls and body. Roller tonging can take as long as 20 or 30 minutes because each mesh must be carefully tonged as described in the roller tonging section. The application of products (designed to protect the hair from heat damage during thermal styling and help prolong the curl's durability) can be applied to each mesh as you systematically work through the hair mesh by mesh. It is important that the meshes are taken in accordance with the direction of the intended style. For example, if the sides are to be dressed away from the face, vertical meshes would be taken at the sides and the tongs directed in such a way that the mesh is wound backwards from the front hairline. The angles at which the meshes are held and directed for roller tonging follows the same principles as when setting the hair using rollers. If the hair is short, roller tonging will normally begin at the front hairline. For long hair, tonging is usually started at the nape, working up towards the front hairline. Providing the curl is slipped off the rod of the tongs carefully and allowed to cool each time, short hair will usually hold the new shape without support. Longer hair will usually need to be held in position (so that the curl does not drop) by securing it in the same manner as you would a stand-up pincurl (see Chapter 5 – Setting) making sure the body of the curl is not disturbed when the clip is positioned. After the roller tonging is completed, remove any clips and dress the hair into shape.

Spiral tonging

The true description of the spiral winding technique is that the hair is wound starting at the roots and not at the points of the hair as in croquignole winding. As spiral curls (ringlets) are most successfully achieved on longer hair, the tonging begins at the nape and works upwards. Small meshes are taken about 2 cm (1 inch) square. The irons are placed in the hair about 7–10 cm (3–4 inches) from the roots with the trough uppermost as in roller tonging. The irons are closed and rolled upwards towards the head while your other hand is gradually feeding the hair into the irons. Slightly open the irons each time the hair is turned so that hair already wound on the irons can be gently nudged up the length of the rod allowing the rest of the hair to be wound evenly along the rod without unnecessary overlap as shown in Figure 7.3. Allow the hair to cool before dressing.

Figure 7.3 Spiral tonging technique

Smoothing with tongs

It is possible to 'iron' unwanted curl from hair using tongs in a smoothing motion. This is a useful technique to use when roller tonging chemically relaxed Afro hair which has a regrowth of naturally curly hair. This technique is possible only if the regrowth is fairly substantial, i.e. more than 4 cm (1.5 inches) because of the risk of burning the scalp when attempting to smooth a shorter regrowth. Meshes of hair are taken in the same manner as for roller tonging. Before following the roller tonging movements, the regrowth is stroked with the rod of the tongs to iron out the unwanted curl. The direction of the strokes should always be away from the roots towards the chemically relaxed hair taking care that the movements are sufficiently controlled so only the natural (virgin) hair is smoothed. Hold the mesh in your fingers while smoothing to control the hair and to ensure sufficient tension is maintained to aid the action of the tongs. Once the regrowth is smoother (it is unlikely that all traces of movement will be removed without subjecting the hair to a damaging amount of heat) immediately continue roller tonging the mesh.

Hair pressing

There are two main types of hair pressing, soft and hard pressing:

- Soft pressing involves pressing the hair once over the entire head with a pressing comb. Soft pressing is also called single comb pressing.

- Hard pressing involves a second pressing procedure over the original soft press. As more heat and mechanical action are used it is easier to cause damage. Use caution until the right skills and confidence have been developed. Hard pressing is also called double comb pressing.

Soft and hard pressings are illustrated in Figure 7.4.

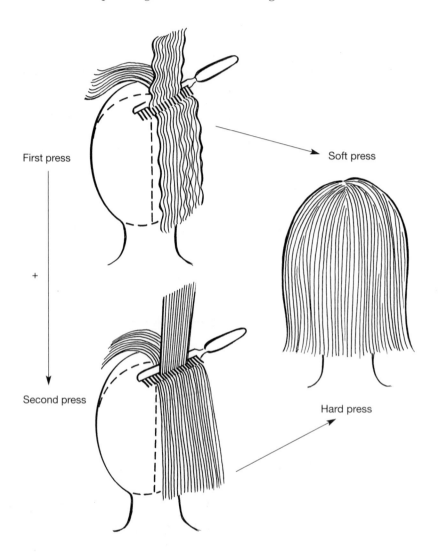

Figure 7.4 The soft press is achieved by pressing the hair once, while the hard press is achieved by pressing the straightened hair a second time

First press

+

Second press

Soft press

Hard press

Soft pressing

1 Shampoo, rinse and towel-dry the hair. Apply pressing oil (for dry, brittle or damaged hair) or pressing cream (lanolin type for normal hair condition, sometimes called cream press) sparingly in sections over the entire head of hair. These oils and creams make it easier for the comb to move through the hair during pressing, causing less mechanical damage (they act as a lubricant and help conduct heat from the comb into the hair, making pressing quicker and more efficient).

2 Comb the hair and section into four quarters, clipping back three sections, leaving the back left (or right) section ready for subsectioning.

3 Heat the pressing comb ready to commence pressing. Before using the comb on the hair, test the heated comb on a piece of white tissue paper before applying it to the hair. If the paper shows signs of scorching (a yellowing or browning of the paper), allow the comb to cool and retest before proceeding with pressing.

4 Starting at the bottom of the left (or right) back section, subsection the hair into shorter partings and work from the nape to the crown. Clip back the hair above the subsections that you are working on, and complete one-quarter of the head at a time. Hair which is fine and sparse can be subsectioned into partings larger than 3.75 cm (1.5 inches) while coarse hair can be subsectioned into smaller partings than 2.5 cm (1 inch) in order to ensure complete heat penetration into the hair.

5 Hold the ends of the hair of the subsection between the middle and index finger of the left hand, and hold the section upward, away from the scalp. Insert the teeth of the pressing comb into the top side of the hair section close to the scalp (about one centimetre or half an inch away) holding the hair strand firmly against the back rod of the comb.

6 Keeping a firm pressure of hair against the back rod of the pressing comb, comb through the hair a short distance while turning the comb away from you so that the hair partly wraps itself around the comb. Maintain the pressure and draw the comb up through the entire hair strand until the hair ends pass through the teeth. This is shown in Figure 7.5. It is the back rod of the comb that actually presses the hair. Repeat this pressing motion a second time on top of the subsection and then reverse the comb and press the subsection once from underneath.

Figure 7.5 The correct way to handle a pressing comb

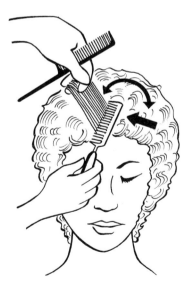

7 Continue pressing over the quarter head section until complete, then press the other three quarter head sections until the entire head has been pressed.

Depending on the result achieved, it may be necessary to repeat pressing to get really smooth results. Coarse, wiry hair will be the most difficult for achieving good pressing results. The second pressing is achieved by repeating steps 2–7. Less pressing oil or cream is required but great care must be taken not to damage the hair.

Touch-ups may be required if parts of the hair begin to revert to their natural curl, as might occur from excessive scalp sweating.

Apply finishing/styling product to the hair near the scalp and brush it through the hair. Style and comb the hair according to the finished look the client desires. Thermal waving, curling or blow-dry styling are all popular.

Using heated rollers

Heated rollers do not operate at the high temperatures of curling tongs or pressing combs. Consequently, fewer hydrogen bonds are broken resulting in softer, less durable movement. Inside heated rollers is a type of wax which melts when heated, thus retaining heat. As the wax cools it sets, and when the roller is cool it is removed from the hair. Heated rollers are very useful for adding body to long hair, preparing the hair for long hair dressing and for quick 'tidying-up' after a set has dropped. They are not particularly effective as completely substituting a cohesive set because the durability of the movement created is not that resilient due to their relatively lower temperature resulting in fewer bonds being broken.

Generally speaking, heated rollers come as sets of anything between twelve and twenty-four rollers. The roller sizes will include large, medium and small and have their own, often colour-coded, clips to secure them in place. Once they are heated, they are put in the hair in the same manner as ordinary rollers but because there are a limited number, larger meshes of hair are taken. If you are using heated rollers on particularly fine or damaged hair which marks easily, it is advisable to cover the spikes of the rollers with a layer of tissue or very fine foam which serves to make the surface of the roller smoother and also acts as a buffer for the heat. When the set is finished, the rollers are left in the hair until they are cool. Cooling will usually take about 15–20 minutes. The rollers are then carefully removed (starting from the bottom and working upwards) so the curl is disturbed as little as possible. The hair is allowed to completely cool for a few moments before the hair is dressed.

Marcel waving technique

Marcel waving was developed during the times when electrically heated tongs were not available. However, equally effective results can be achieved by following these movements using modern electric tongs. Unlike the way of positioning tongs for roller tonging with the trough placed on top of the hair, when Marcel waving, the trough is placed *underneath* the mesh of hair. Figure 7.6 shows a step by step to achieving a Marcel wave using traditional waving irons.

1 Comb the hair thoroughly and take a mesh which is approximately 5 cm (2 inches) wide and 1 cm (half an inch) deep. Hold the mesh in position for waving either with your fingers or a comb. Begin by closing the irons on the mesh with the trough on the underneath. Make sure the edge of the trough nearest to you makes contact with the hair first. If both edges close on the hair simultaneously, the hair will be marked with two ridges. Gently close the irons and at the same time, roll the tongs towards the head while at the same time directing them to the right. Allow the heat to penetrate the hair and then unroll the irons. You have now formed the first crest.

2 Position the irons so that the edge of the trough furthest from you fits exactly with the underside of the crest. Gently close the irons and roll them a half turn under. Allow the heat to penetrate and open the irons.

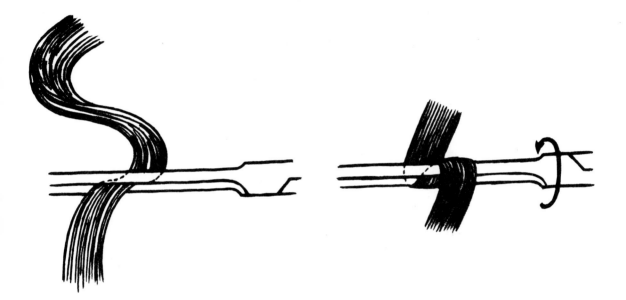

3 Slide the irons down the hair about 3 cm (1.5 inches) and they are now in position for forming the next crest.

4 Make the second crest following the same pattern as used before except that the hair is directed to the left this time.

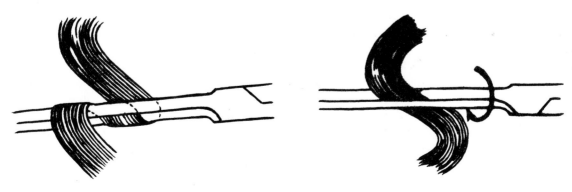

5 The finished wave shape.

Figure 7.6 Marcel waving technique

To join up waves, a piece of already waved hair is used as a guide to ensure the crests of the waves are evenly spaced and that the wave pattern across the head is even. Use only warm irons for joining up Marcel waves because too much heat on previously waved hair will cause the wave pattern to become distorted. Joining up waves using part of a previously waved piece of hair is shown in Figure 7.7.

Figure 7.7 Joining up Marcel waves

Using other thermal equipment

In Chapter 2 a number of other thermal styling tools are included with an explanation of their use. It is possible to combine the use of more than one type of thermal styling tool on the same head to create interesting effects, particularly for photographic and fashion work. For example, the hair can be waved using the New Wave tool while the fringe can be reshaped using a hot brush.

Safe working guide – thermal styling

- Use thermal styling equipment only on clean, dry hair.
- Make sure your hands are dry and that the area where you are working is away from water.
- NEVER use any electrical appliances which are faulty or in need of repair. You should always visibly check the appliance for a frayed lead, damaged plug, etc. *before* connecting it to the electricity supply.
- If using thermal styling equipment which is not thermostatically controlled, or you are dealing with fine and/or damaged hair, always test the temperature of the appliance *before* placing in the hair.
- Take the necessary precautions to prevent damage to the client's hair and/or skin.
- Make sure you know the first aid treatment for burns.
- Regularly clean the appliance and have it professionally serviced.
- NEVER place hot appliances in bags or cupboards.
- Use vulcanite combs in combination with thermal styling equipment because they have more resistance to heat than those made of plastic.
- NEVER place hot appliances on surfaces which are not heat resistant.
- Be alert when using hot equipment if children are present in the salon: they may pick up the appliance out of curiosity and burn themselves.

Revision Questions

1 When were thermal styling tools first used to reshape hair?

2 What is the name of the French hairdresser who revolutionised the use of curling irons?

3 Which bonds are affected in the hair during thermal styling?

4 Draw a diagram of a pair of tongs and label the parts.

5 What is croquignole winding?

6 What will cause the points of hair to be buckled when tonging?

7 What is placed between the client's scalp and tongs during tonging?

8 How should tongs be positioned and directed during roller tonging?

9 What is spiral winding?

10 Give an example of when you would use tongs for smoothing.

11 What is the difference in the results of a soft and hard press?

12 On what type of hair would pressing combs be used?

13 Why do heated rollers not break as many bonds as curling tongs or pressing combs?

14 When creating Marcel waves, is the trough of the irons placed above or underneath the mesh of hair?

15 What is used as a guide for joining up Marcel waves?

Advanced Questions

1 With the aid of diagrams, explain the physical change in hair during thermal styling.

2 Describe the effect achieved of the following thermal styling tools (use diagrams if necessary):

(i) crimpers

(ii) pressing comb

(iii) spiral tongs

3 List the precautions to be taken when thermally styling damaged hair.

4 Draw and label diagrams of the following thermal styling tools:

(i) Marcel waving irons

(ii) modern day tongs

(iii) pressing comb.

Chapter 8

SPECIALISED HAIR WORK

Introduction

All hairdressers want to be able to satisfy their clients' needs by being able to meet each individual client's requirements. If the hairdresser is unable to carry out a particular request, it could result in the loss of a client to another salon where that service is available.

Styling long hair is often a frightening prospect for the hairdresser, but it need not be. We all remember the people who can work with long hair as if it were second nature – the ones who have a 'feel' for the hair. If you are not one of that minority, read on! This chapter looks at simple ways of achieving styles for long hair and also at adding false hair to create stunning looks on shorter hair. Once the principles of these skills are mastered, only the hairdresser's imagination will limit the originality and intricacy of the work that is produced.

A simple conversion

Clients with long curly hair may ask you to do something different for a special occasion. Here is a simple way of achieving a look on naturally curly hair which requires no backcombing.

Verelle Hairdressing – step by step

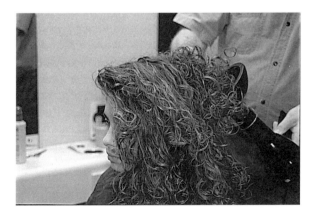

1 Naturally curly hair is scrunch-dried using a diffuser attachment.

2 The finished look after drying.

3 Take a panel of hair at the crown which is approximately 5 cm by 2 cm (2 inches by 1 inch). It is important that you do not pull or comb the hair too much because too much handling will straighten the curl. If you need to use a comb, use a wide-toothed one or a rake. If you are working with permed hair, the perm should be fairly new because you will need curl and body at the roots.

4 Divide this panel of hair into three and make a plait. Secure the plait using a band. This plait is going to act as a foundation for securing the grips.

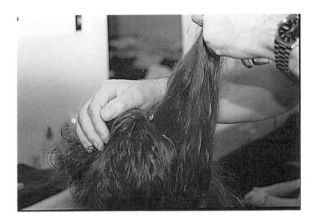

5 Using only your fingers (to avoid straightening the curl) and handling the hair gently, pick up fairly large meshes and take them up to the crown. Now, twist the mesh and hold it in position for securing with a grip. Use your fingers to separate and place the curls. Continue bringing up meshes in this way remembering that you should twist all the meshes in the same direction.

6 You will notice that some of the hair has been dressed asymmetrically and that the stylist made optimum use of the hair's natural curl.

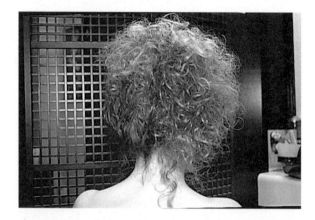

7 This is the back view showing the gentle twists.

French pleat

Verelle Hairdressing – step by step

1 Permed hair with long layers has been dried and then set on rollers in the direction of the intended style before being put under a hood drier for 5 minutes. The rollers have been positioned so that the hair at the front is directed to the side; the hair at the sides has been set away from the face; the rollers at the back are wound upwards and clips have been used on these rollers to make sure they do not loosen.

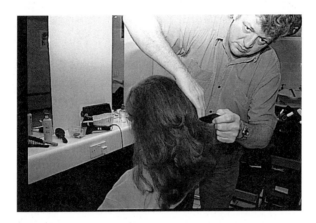

2 The hair is backcombed in the direction of the style and then smoothed out using either a wide-toothed comb, rake or pick to avoid pulling out the backcombing. The hair should be smoothed and directed according to the shape of the finished style.

3 Once the hair is in position, a line of grips is placed from the nape up to the crown. The hair at the nape should be directed upwards and across because this is more flattering to the neck and hairline than simply taking it across to the side. The grips are placed so that they overlap each other for extra hold and the last grip at the crown is placed downwards. Notice how the line of grips are placed to form a slight curve; this curve will give the vertical roll a better shape.

4 The loose hair is now folded on itself to form a cone-shaped roll; notice that the roll should be closer to the head at the nape and becomes gradually fuller as it reaches the crown.

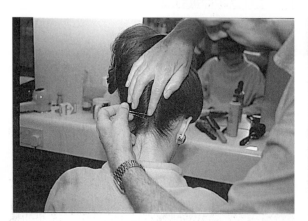

5 Fine pins are used to secure the roll in place and it is important that these are placed so that they hold the hair firmly and are not too noticeable. First, the pin picks up a few hairs and is directed at an angle towards the stylist.

6 The pin is then turned so that it comes back and is pushed into the roll.

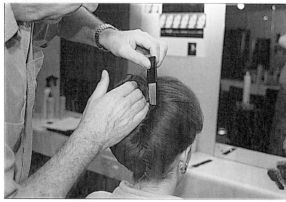

7 The roll is then secured with fine pins all the way up the roll.

8 A pick can be used to help tuck the ends of the hair inside the roll.

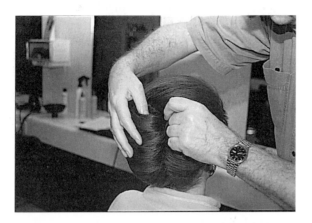

9 The top will probably need flattening slightly and the front hair will need to be blended into the style while checking the balance of the shape in the mirror.

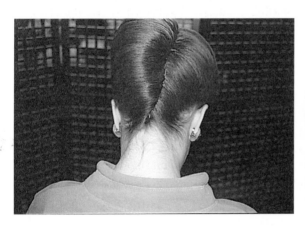 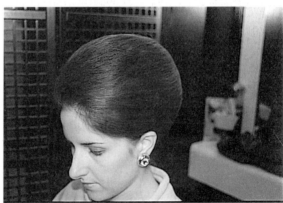

10 Here is the back of the finished style.

11 The profile of the finished style. Both photos show the shape and polished finish.

Horizontal roll

Verelle Haidressing – step by step

1 After setting on velcro or heated rollers (as both of these prevent breaks from appearing in the final dressing), the hair is brushed through. A parting is then made around the head; this parting is where the roll will be positioned so it is worth spending time checking that it is evenly balanced and is in the right place.

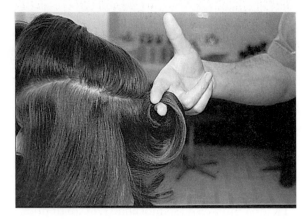

2 To check whether the parting is in the correct place, hold a piece of hair to be made into the roll up to the parting as shown in the photo. There should be enough hair to allow the end to be tucked in and gripped.

3 The top hair is dressed first by backcombing and then smoothing into shape. Grips are then used to secure the top hair in place at the back just below where the parting was made. To make this really secure, the grips on each side of this piece of hair should be pointing towards the centre.

4 The roll should be started with the loose hair in the centre of the nape. To ensure the backcombing will not show, the meshes should be backcombed on the top because the hair will be rolled upwards. Once the mesh is smoothed out and the ends of the hair are folded inside the roll, it is held in position and secured with grips. Notice that the mesh of hair has been spread out so that the widest part is through the centre. This ensures that there will be no gaps or breaks in the roll.

5 The hair at the sides is then backcombed, smoothed and gripped in the same way.

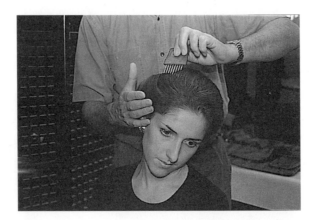

6 Using a pick, the shape of the style is then adjusted to ensure it is evenly balanced.

7 The finished horizontal roll.

Plaiting techniques with long hair

Plaiting (or braiding) long hair is a skill which can be used to create interesting and stunning looks. Here is a step by step to show you a method of plaiting long hair which is probably the most popular of all plaits.

Verelle Hairdressing – step by step

Step 1
A triangular section of hair is taken at the top front and divided into three.

Step 2
The three strands are plaited by taking the outside strands and crossing them over the centre strand. No extra hair is picked up and added to the plait at this stage.

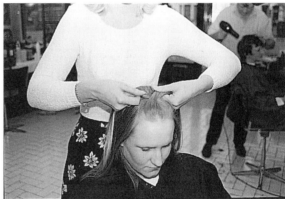

Step 3
Hair is now picked up and joined with the strands being taken over the centre. If you crossed the left hand side into the centre when you began your plait, you will pick up from the left side first.

Step 4
Hair on the right hand side is now picked up with the fingers and joined with the strand before taking it over the centre.

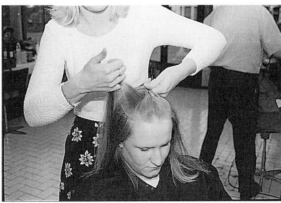

Step 5

The picking up of hair and joining it with the strands continues. Notice how close the stylist's hands are to the head. If the hands are too far away from the head the plait will be too loose and saggy. It is also important to make sure the client's head is bent forward when you reach the back of the head so that the plait sits close to the head.

Step 6

The last few pieces of hair are taken and joined with the strands to complete the plait.

Step 7

When there is no more hair left to pick up, the plait is finished by simply crossing the outside strands over the centre strand.

Step 8

The plait can either be tied and left to hang loose or can be tucked under and gripped for an alternative look.

Two-strand braid (Figure 8.1)

Figure 8.1 How to make a
two-strand braid (1–4)

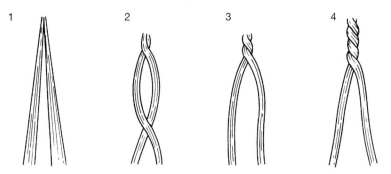

1 Separate the section into two equal parts.
2 Cross the sections over each other.
3 Continue crossing the hair strands over each other, being careful to
  maintain even tension on the strands.
4 Cross the strands over each other along the entire length. When you
  reach the ends, secure with a pin, or tie with thread without letting go.

Three-strand braid (Figure 8.2)

This is perhaps the most common of all braiding techniques.

Figure 8.2 How to make a
three-strand braid (1–4)

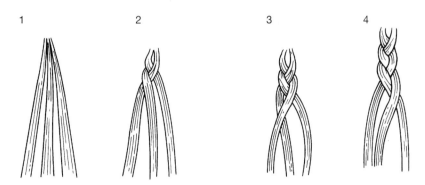

1 Separate the section into three equal parts.
2 Begin by crossing one of the strands on the outside across the one in the
  centre. Then cross the other outside strand across the centre one. In the
  diagram, you can see that the strand on the right side is the next one to
  be crossed over to the centre.
3 In this diagram it is the strand on the left that now needs to be
  crossed over to the centre. Keep the tension even to produce a regular
  shaped braid.
4 Continue crossing the outside strands into the centre until you reach the
  ends. Secure with a piece of thread or a pin.

Four-strand braid (Figure 8.3)

The four-strand braid looks very intricate but is really quite easy to master if you study the diagrams carefully.

Figure 8.3 How to make a four-strand braid (1–5)

1 Separate the section into four equal parts.
2 Start braiding with the two centre strands, taking the left strand over the right one.
3 The side strand is then brought to the centre by bringing the one on the right side *above* one of the first two strands, and the strand on the left side is taken *under* the other one.
4 Diagrams 4(a), (b) and (c) show how this is continued along the hair length with the two centre strands always being crossed in the same manner as in number 2.
5 The finished braid is shown in this diagram. It can be fastened by a covered elastic hair band or ribbon. A needle with a large eye can be used to weave coloured thread or ribbon through the braid to create a stunning effect for special occasions. This looks particularly effective if it has a metallic coating.

Eight-strand braid (Figure 8.4)

This braid is more difficult to master because you will probably feel that you need an extra pair of hands. Braiding with this number of strands is much easier to do if you have somebody to help you hold and control the hair as you are working. An eight-strand braid will be shown at its best on very long hair.

1 Separate the section into eight equal parts.
2 Begin by crossing the four centre strands, two by two. Take the strands on the right over those on the left (study the diagram carefully).
3 Weave these strands out to the edges by taking them over and under the other strands.

Figure 8.4 How to make an eight-strand braid (1–6)

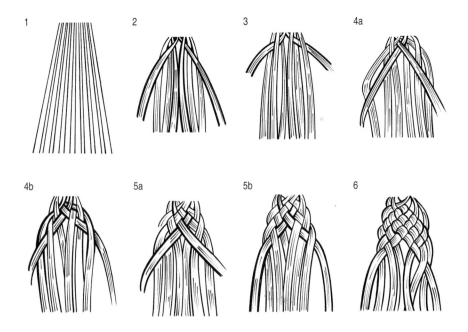

4 Diagrams 4(a) and (b) now take the two centre strands again and cross these left over right, as shown in 4(a) and (b).

5 Continue weaving out towards the edges, keeping an even, slight tension to make the braid even, as shown in 5(a) and (b).

6 Continue in this way to the hair points, securing the ends with thread or pins. Once you have mastered the eight-strand braid, try a sixteen-strand braid following the same pattern as you did with this one.

Plaiting technique with shorter hair

Plaited styles are also possible on clients whose hair is not very long. Here, you are shown how to create a built-up plaited style on smooth, dry hair for a client with chin-length hair.

Verelle Hairdressing – step by step

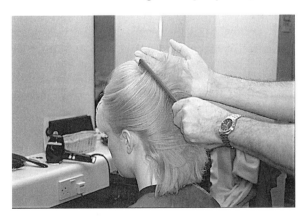

1 To test whether the client's hair is long enough for this look, see if it reaches the point where it is to be secured. Beware of making life difficult for yourself by attempting to do this style on a person with hair which is too long because the excess hair will cause problems. It is also easier to handle the hair if it is not freshly shampooed; freshly shampooed hair tends to be more slippery and fly away so is more difficult to control.

2 The front top section of the hair is dressed first. Begin by dividing off a section of hair and check that it is evenly balanced by looking in the mirror. To give the style some height, the hair is backcombed in the direction of the intended style, i.e. backwards and away from the face.

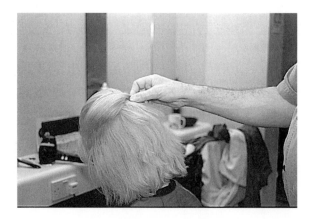

3 Once the hair is smoothed and is in the correct position to cover the parting around the edge of the section, it is secured so that the grips on each side of the section are pointing towards the centre.

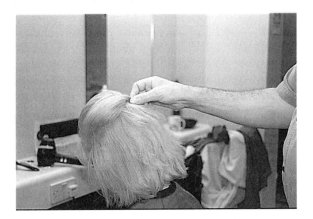

4 Take half the hair at one side and backcomb on the underneath. Smooth out the hair with a large-toothed comb and position it so that it can be secured with a grip past the centre of the head.

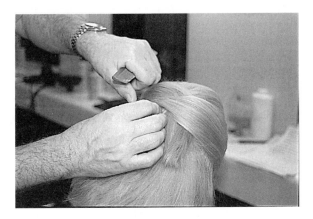

5 Continue taking sections of hair in this manner working on each side of the head in turn.

6 The final section is treated in exactly the same way with the hair being directed upwards. The ends of the hair are tucked neatly inside and the final mesh is secured in place.

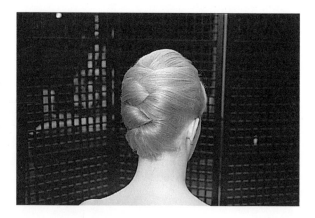

7 The finished built-up plait.

Working with postiche

Pieces of hair work such as full wigs and hairpieces are called postiche. The popularity of postiche fluctuates but it is particularly useful for theatrical and film work, session work and competitions. Other uses for postiche include the wearing of wigs in certain occupations like the legal profession (although these are not normally produced by wigmakers connected with hairdressing), those disguising hair loss as a result of illness or the natural thinning of their hair, and those who wear wigs simply for convenience, fun or a change.

Postiche is either hand-made by a wigmaker (most expensive), partly by machine, or completely by machine. The hair used to make postiche can be human, animal or synthetic. Human hair, particularly virgin hair, is the most expensive and is obtained in the form of cuttings and combings. The most expensive human hair is virgin blonde hair because it is the most rare; this usually comes from Germany. The best quality dark and white hair comes from Spain and Northern Italy (Tuscany region) while France is the source of the best quality auburn and brown hair. Coarser and consequently cheaper hair comes from China and Japan. Postiche made from animal hair, used mainly for competition and special effects (it is too soft to be used for normal wear), is obtained from a species of ox (called a yak and native to Tibet) or mohair from the Angora goat. Nylon (synthetic) hair is the cheapest, is available in any colour and is used for mannequins in window displays and some special effects. If used as a substitute to a human hair wig, it has the disadvantages of being difficult to restyle and can be uncomfortable to wear because nylon does not allow the scalp to 'breathe'. Postiche is formed of either 'weft' which describes hairs that have been woven on silks, thread and/or wire and then sewn together, or 'knotted' pieces when just a few hairs at a time have been carefully knotted to a foundation base made of net, silk or gauze using a special knotting hook.

Full wigs are not always what the hairdresser needs to create a particular look. There are many different forms of postiche at the disposal of the creative hairdresser and smaller pieces of postiche with such names as 'diamond mesh', 'pincurls', 'switches', 'double loop clusters' and 'crêpe pads' can be used to add length, bulk and lift to styles. It is unlikely that the average salon would have the space, inclination, nor the necessary equipment to make postiche to order, although some salons are able to offer a cleaning and simple alterations and repair service. The art of wig-making is a specialist field, and most wigmakers will work in the film and theatre industries or be commissioned by the National Health Service to make postiche for patients who have lost their hair through illness or scarring. There are a few places where wigmaking can be learnt but postiche is very easily available from specialist providers.

Cleaning, preparing and securing postiche

Cleaning

The cleaning method used for postiche is dictated by the fibre from which it is made. Synthetic (nylon) postiche can safely be cleaned by gently swishing it in a solution of lukewarm water and shampoo. After thorough rinsing, it is shaken to remove the excess moisture and left to dry naturally. Synthetic postiche should never be combed or brushed when it is damp as this will cause damage and make it frizz. Any movement or curl (which is permanent and already in the fibre when it is manufactured) will return when the fibre is completely dry and it is then that the postiche can be brushed into shape.

For postiche made of human or animal hair, washing with water and shampoo is not recommended because it would cause shrinkage and loosening of the weaving or knotting and will tangle the hair. Instead, special cleansing agents for wigs and hairpieces are used. It is usually necessary to clean and dry the postiche in a well-ventilated area because the cleaning fluid may give off fumes which can cause drowsiness. The postiche is placed in a bowl of the cleansing agent (full wigs should be turned inside out before cleaning so that the base is sufficiently treated) so that it is completely submerged. It should be left in the fluid for several minutes (to allow the cleaning agent to loosen the dirt) before dipping the postiche in and out of the fluid so that it runs through the hair from the roots to points. Remember, it should be treated with the same amount of care that you would give to a cashmere sweater. If the postiche is particularly dirty, you may need to repeat the process with fresh fluid. Once clean, the postiche is gently squeezed and shaken and then carefully pegged on an outside line to dry.

Preparation

Only human or animal hair can be successfully styled because postiche made from synthetic fibre (i.e. nylon) will not curl satisfactorily using rollers, blow-driers or thermal appliances and could melt if subjected to too much heat. To prepare human and animal hair postiche for styling, it should be carefully positioned and secured onto a malleable block using dressmaking or 'T' pins. Wigmakers call mounting a wig in this way as 'blocking' a wig.

Malleable blocks are canvas covered and head shaped. They are shaped similarly to the human head (and are available in different sizes, the average size being 54 cm in circumference) and are stuffed with sawdust. A malleable block should be protected by a covering of tissue or fine cotton lawn before a wig is mounted onto it. The 'T' pins take their name from their shape and are used to secure postiche to the malleable block but dressmaking pins should be used if working with a wig which has very fine hair lace (a very delicate type of flesh coloured netting at the front of the wig with the purpose of forming an undetectable bond with the forehead, temples and sides of the face).

For a full wig, the securing pins should carefully be placed at each side (on the edge of the ear peak), one at the centre front and two at the nape. To protect the delicate hair lace from being damaged by pins, a band of galloon tape (a type of tape used in the making of postiche) should be placed between the pins and the hair lace. The wig must always be checked that it is properly positioned by checking that the sides of the wig are level on both sides. Smaller postiche are similarly secured.

Once the wig is mounted, it should be carefully brushed to remove any tangles and to loosen debris. Bristle brushes are best for working on postiche. During setting or blow-drying, great care should be taken not to wet or tear the foundation or hair lace or loosen the hair. If using rollers, choose smooth ones which can be secured with either normal setting pins or 'T' pins. Avoid using clips to secure pincurls because they can mark the hair; use 'T' pins or two fine pins (crossed over each other) instead. If you are finger waving a wig, galloon tape can be carefully positioned in the trough (hollow) of the waves and in the direction of the movement to maintain their shape without fear of marking or disturbing the hair. The galloon tape can be secured with either 'T' pins or dressmaking pins.

Styling products can be safely used providing they are not allowed to wet the foundation which would be as damaging as putting the postiche under a tap. Wetting the postiche is done by dipping a comb in warm water and combing through the hair while avoiding wetting the foundation and hair lace. If the postiche is set, it is covered with a hairnet and dried under a warm hairdrier (although proper wig departments would have a special oven which is used to dry postiche). Once the hair is completely dry it is usual practice to dress each curl and movement individually rather than brush everything through to remove any roller marks as you would on a client's head. The dressing is checked for balance and that no grips and pins are visible. A little hairspray can be used if required. If it is not to be worn straightaway, it can be kept either on the malleable block (in a dry atmosphere) or carefully padded and wrapped in tissue paper and stored in a box.

Securing

To put on a full wig, you should first comb the client's hair away from the front hairline. Sometimes, a stocking is placed over the client's hair to keep it flat and help prevent the wig from slipping. The wig is then positioned and held on the front hairline while gently easing it over the crown area to the nape. (In salons, it is common practice to leave a small amount of the client's hair out of the wig and this is then combed over the front of the wig to give a more natural effect and to disguise the wig's foundation). Additional securing may not always be necessary but if you do want to secure it really firmly, before putting the wig on, you should form neat pincurls at the sides, nape and centre front hairline in the client's dry hair and secure the pincurls with two grips which are crossed. Once the wig is in place, fine pins are gently eased through the foundation to the pincurls below, ensuring the wig will not move. Smaller pieces of postiche may have combs sewn in the base but these are often ineffective and they may need to be secured with grips and pins to ensure they do not slip. The positioning of any postiche is important to create the correct balance in the finished style. Once the position of the hairpiece is decided, make a small section of hair in the middle of its intended position and make this into a pincurl and secure with two crossed grips. This forms a good foundation for gripping the hairpiece in position. When using pins and grips for photographic work, always use ones which match the hair colour you are working with and choose ones which have a matt rather than a shiny finish to avoid them glinting and being detected under studio lights.

Hair extensions

Simon Forbes at the Antenna salon in Kensington, London, pioneered the idea of adding acrylic fibre to heads of hair to create stunningly interesting looks.

Monofibre extensions come in bright colours such as pink, blue and green, or more neutral shades to blend with the wearer's natural hair colour. They can be used for creating wild looks, or used to add length and bulk to short hair which can then be cut to style for less outrageous clients. They are extremely versatile.

Basically, the false fibre is attached to the client's real hair by braiding and then heating the fibre (which melts) to form a strong seal. Some salons use a flame to do this, but on grounds of safety this should not be done, so stick to an electric apparatus like the one illustrated in Figure 8.5.

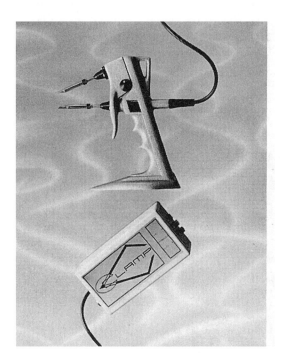

Figure 8.5 The Clamp is an electric implement used to seal monofibre to the hair; it is thermostatically controlled and safe to use (Courtesy Antenna Ltd)

Extensions can be attached in many imaginative ways. The most popular are called 'warlocks', 'ragtails', 'dreadlocks', 'cable curls', 'monofines' (see Figure 8.6) and 'bobtails'. Each technique creates a different look which is guaranteed by Antenna to last for a minimum of three months. As its clients come from as far afield as Switzerland and Sweden, it is not unusual for the extensions to be worn in the hair for as long as a year. However, Antenna does emphasise that the extensions are harder to remove if they are left in the hair for such long periods.

How are extensions applied?

In an average situation, sixty extensions would be applied. Attaching extensions takes a long time, usually over two hours, and requires two stylists because two pairs of hands are needed. One pair of hands act as the 'control' hands, while the others use a four-stem braid to join the fibre with the client's own hair (see technical tips, below).

Once the fibre is attached to the real hair by the braiding, it must be sealed in position. This could be done with a naked flame, such as a candle. However, this chars the fibre rather than just melting it, and is also a fire hazard in the salon. A special piece of salon equipment called the 'Clamp' has been designed for the sealing of monofibre extensions. It is illustrated in Figure 8.5 and has the following advantages:

Figure 8.6 The 'Dodger', a soft-textured style that remains a definite shape: monofibres have been scattered through the hair, then clipper-cut free hand (Courtesy Antenna Ltd)

- It can be used to seal the finer extensions called monofines.
- It can be used to attach extensions much closer to the scalp than a naked flame.
- It reduces the operating time.
- It creates a more professional image.
- It melts rather than chars monofibre.

The Clamp is hand-cast and finished, and is made from solid aluminium. The two nickel-plated tips are heated electrically and can be detached for cleaning with something like fine emery paper. They are thermostatically controlled by three buttons on the control unit. The trigger on the Clamp controls the movement of the two heated tips. When the trigger is squeezed the tips close on the monofibre, sealing the extension in place by melting it onto the natural hair.

How are extensions removed?

Extensions take just as long to remove as they do to apply. The bond made by the heat is broken by twisting it from side to side, and the braid is then unravelled until the monofibre is separated from the natural hair. The extensions could be removed at home by the client, with the aid of a friend.

What advice should be given to the client who has extensions?

It is a good idea to produce an after-care leaflet which can be taken away by the client. It should contain the following information and advice:

- Allow two weeks before shampooing and then use cool water and massage gently.
- Brushing or combing is not advisable.
- General 'bunching' normally occurs within a period of two weeks. This is considered to be part of the look and style of extensions.
- To avoid tangling at the roots, it is advisable to run the fingers gently through the roots every couple of weeks.
- Explain how the extensions can be removed at home.
- Extensions will loosen due to natural hair growth.

Technical tips

- Lift extensions at the front of the head so that you can cut them over your hands. This will prevent hitting the eyebrows or eyelashes while clipper cutting.
- Razor cutting can make the extensions look more real as they blend in with the natural hair better.
- Cut monofibre extensions with a separate pair of scissors which you do not value too highly. The monofibre will dull scissor blades.
- Cut up bales of monofibre using ordinary needlework scissors
- When creating a haircut use a free-hand approach, relying on what you can see and feel.
- Encourage staff to wear extensions in different styles; they are suitable for many types of clients.
- Make extensions thicker at the back of the head. Concentrate your fine extensions on the sides and front of the head.
- Advise clients that extensions tend to moult for up to 24 hours after the service. They should not fall out, so make your clients aware of this in case they come back complaining – that is never good for business!
- Monofibre does not absorb tint. If ever you bleach hair with extensions scattered throughout the hair, rinse the head four or five times more than normal after bleaching. Any bleach remaining under the extension could cause breakage.
- You might find it beneficial to take deposits on appointments for extensions if it is not a regular client. With two stylists involved it means booking out over two hours for each operator. Someone who is unwilling to leave a small deposit (or even a post-dated cheque) is unlikely to turn up for the appointment.

Hair ornamentation

Ornaments are worn in hair to enhance and embellish hairstyles and include jewellery, flowers, slides, ribbons and thread. There is such a wide selection of hair ornaments available that few hairdressers bother making their own. However, for some competition and fashion work there is no substitute for making your own ornaments from small pieces of postiche and it is worth the time and effort to create unique hair ornaments. Here are some examples of hair ornaments.

Flowers

Keep flowers in fresh water until they are needed and then dry the stems thoroughly before cutting the stem to the length required. If possible, thread fine wire up the stem to make it easier to position and secure in the hair. Flowers which make pretty and effective decoration include gypsophila, freesias, carnations, roses, daisies and lilies of the valley. Some artificial flowers are very realistic; they have the advantage of being easier to manipulate and do not wilt. Dried flowers and grasses also make ideal hair decoration.

Ribbons and thread

These can be intertwined with the hair during plaiting. Seal the ends of cut ribbons with hairspray or clear adhesive to help prevent unsightly fraying. Always iron ribbons if they are creased. Use a large blunt sewing needle (e.g. a bobbin) to sew ribbons and threads through the hair or attach by tying to grips.

Beads

Individual beads or clusters of beads, available from most haberdashery departments and craft shops, can be sewn into the hair using a large sewing needle. Choose a sewing thread which matches the hair colour. Strings of bead (i.e. necklaces and bracelets) can also be used to effect. Beads can be glued to combs and slides to make other interesting ornaments.

Feathers

These can be bought from most craft or art shops and are available in all sizes and colours. Feathers can be easily glued to combs and slides which are then positioned in the hair or can be placed individually into a style.

Jewellery

Never discard unwanted jewellery because you can recycle it by making your own hair ornaments.

Head-dresses and tiaras

These are usually worn for special occasions such as weddings. If you are doing the hair of a bride, always suggest that she visits the salon before the 'big day' so that you can practise the style and get the positioning of any head-dress or other hair ornamentation absolutely right. Expensive tiaras and other forms of head-dress should always be protected from hairspray as it will dull the shine and possibly tarnish any gems and stones.

Postiche

Ornaments made of hair can be stunning. Consider making flowers and other shapes from real or synthetic hair. It is easy to obtain a variety of prepared plaits of hair which can then be fixed in the hair.

Other ornaments

By looking around craft shops you will come across a range of things which will make suitable hair ornaments. Such materials include raffia, wool and sequins.

Competition work

Some of the most innovative and creative styles are to be seen on competition floors and it can be very exciting to watch competitors in action. Competition work is not every hairdresser's idea of fun. It enforces self-discipline, stretches the imagination, places the competitor and model under pressure and rigorously examines the competitor's practical and creative skills.

Competitions vary from those designed for entrants who are relatively new to the industry to the more challenging for those with more experience. The UK has a competition squad for both ladies' and mens' competitions who compete on an international basis against other elite teams in the World Championships. Many competition entrants start by competing in an inter-salon or local event before progressing to national and international competitions.

Rules

The work to be executed for a particular competition will be clearly set out in the competition's rules. For example, the rules will state who is eligible to take part, the type of style or look to be executed and the time allowed and will normally mention the prizes for the winners. Other rules will set out things like whether ornamentation, postiche and colour is allowed, what electrical styling equipment (if any) is permitted on the competition floor, how much hair needs to be removed if it is a cutting competition and the degree of preparation that is allowed before the start of the competition. It cannot be over-stressed that competitors need to conform to these rules. Failing to comply with the rules may result in marks being deducted or complete disqualification.

Scrutineers

People designated as 'scrutineers' at competitions check that competitors comply with the rules before and during the competition. For example, if the rules state that the model must arrive on the competition floor with her hair set, ready for dressing out, using a minimum of eight rollers or pincurls, the scrutineers will check that this is the case by inspecting each model in turn before the competition starts. The scrutineer will make a note of the competitor's table number if rules have been broken and the judges will make a decision on the severity of the offence and the penalty to be issued.

Judges

A panel of judges will be recruited by the competition organisers to award marks used to place the winning competitors. Judges are normally 'hidden away' while the actual competition is in progress to ensure they do not see which model belongs to which competitor so marking is fair. All competitors are issued with a 'table number' which is displayed at the position where they are working to ensure anonymity. The model may also be asked to wear or hold the same number. The judging takes place at the end of the competition after the competitors have had time to remove their tools and equipment from the competition table and have arranged their model in a pose which shows their work at its best. Competitors are not permitted on the floor during judging.

Adjudication

The judges will have been briefed by the 'adjudicator' who is the judge given the authority to make overriding decisions, as in the case of a tie or marks deducted as a penalty for breaking the rules. Depending on the nature of the competition, the judges will usually be marking technical skill, artistry and innovation. Often, judges are also asked to award marks for the 'total look' of the models. This means they will be judging how well the competitor has interpreted the competition's theme in the appropriate use of make-up, accessories and clothes the model is wearing. For example, if a competition is billed as 'Ladies' Evening Style' it would be necessary for competitors to ensure their models were appropriately attired in evening dress, while for a 'Commercial Blow Dry' competition it can be assumed that models need to be wearing fashionable day clothes. Once the judges have completed their marking, they will leave the floor to go off and add up the marks. At this point, it is usual for the models to be asked to parade so that the audience has a chance of seeing all the competitors' work. It always seems like an eternity waiting for the results and is a particularly nerve-racking time for competitors, their models and supporters alike. The competitors with the highest scores will be placed in the winning positions and are normally announced in reverse order. This is the moment when for some competitors their dreams are realised and for others there are feelings of great disappointment. It must be remembered that it takes a certain amount of courage to enter hairdressing competitions and to expose yourself to the judgements and criticisms of others. No matter whether they are placed or not, every competitor and model deserves credit for entering a competition and for all the hours they have both put in practising for the event.

Helpful hints for competition work

Models

Competitors need to choose their model carefully. Models should have good skin, preferably be taller than average and of slim build, and have good posture. The texture of their hair and their hairlines should be suitable for the work you intend to do and they should not be averse to hair colour or other necessary treatments. Models need to be available for regular practice sessions, be available for the date of the actual competition and feel confident enough to do your work justice when they are on the competition floor.

Competitors

Competitors need to devote several hours a week leading up to the competition to practising on their model. They need to have patience, energy and resourcefulness; sketches and drawings of the style may need to be made by the competitor to explore the initial style concept and record the progressive development of these ideas. Competitors should examine the rules so that these are correctly interpreted and not broken. They decide the clothes to be worn by the model and either make them or arrange for loan if necessary. Competitors should consider their model at all times.

Historical styles

Historical styles depict an individual person from history or the general style of a historical period. Creating historical styles is most often done by those in theatre and film work but it is not uncommon for a client to request a particular historical look when invited to a theme or fancy dress party. If you are asked to create a particular look, you will invariably need to do some research to ensure the look is sufficiently authentic.

This research will probably take the form of going to a library and looking through a variety of books. A librarian will often be on hand to offer assistance and point you towards the most relevant sources of information. History books will not always prove to be the most useful resource although they are often a good starting point. For example, if you wanted to research Marilyn Monroe, you might come across some helpful pictures in books covering famous celebrities and the films of Hollywood. There are specialist books which include a comprehensive guide to historical hairstyles, head-dresses and make-up. If these are not available in your library, they can usually be ordered by the librarian for you, but this may take several weeks.

Picture and art galleries form another useful source for research material. Remember that long ago, before cameras were invented, paintings were the 'photographs'. If you are unable to visit a gallery, it may be able to send you a set of postcards (there will be a charge) showing the work of a particular artist or period.

Films and TV programmes set in a particular time in history will also prove helpful but do remember that some of the portrayed styles may not be authentic. This is because some film stars would never consider wearing a totally authentic look, neither would a producer always insist upon it. In the film *Cleopatra*, starring Elizabeth Taylor in the title role, her hair and make-up were quite convincing. However, she would have looked out of place if compared to other Egyptian women of similar standing at that time. Conversely, some drama series produced, particularly those by British film and TV companies, can boast the most authentic interpretations of specific periods and are the envy of the industry.

Once you have done your research, it is a good idea to keep notes of your findings and any sketches or photocopies in a file for future use.

Famous historical dressings likely to be requested of the salon-based hairdresser include: Cleopatra (69–30 BC), Elizabeth I (1533–1603), Marie Antoinette (1755–1793), Queen Victoria (1819–1901), Rudolph Valentino (1895–1926), Billie Holiday (1915–1959), Marilyn Monroe (1926–1962), Elvis Presley (1935–1977) and Buddy Holly (1936–1959).

<table>
<tr><td>

**Revision
Questions**

</td><td>

1 In which direction are the rollers placed at the sides and back when preparing hair for a French pleat?

2 When the hair has been backcombed for a French pleat, why is a wide-toothed comb, rake or pick used to smooth the hair into position?

3 What is the benefit to the appearance of the client's neck if the hair is swept upwards at the nape when gripping the hair in position for a French pleat?

4 How are the pins inserted to secure a French pleat so that they hold it firmly while being unnoticeable?

5 How should the stylist judge the ideal position for a horizontal roll?

6 When securing the first piece of hair which makes a horizontal roll, why should both grips point towards the centre?

7 Why are the meshes of hair backcombed on the top when making a horizontal roll?

8 When plaiting to the head, why is it important that the stylist's hands are held close to the scalp?

9 What is postiche?

10 Name four different types of postiche.

11 How would you clean postiche made from

  (i) synthetic hair

  (ii) human or animal hair?

12 If using a small piece of postiche such as a diamond mesh, how is the hair prepared to ensure the added piece will have a good foundation and will not move?

13 Where would you go to research a particular historical period or famous person?

</td></tr>
<tr><td>

**Advanced
Questions**

</td><td>

1 With the aid of diagrams, explain how to style hair into a French pleat.

2 Find out all you can about postiche and produce a mini project to show how it can be used to achieve a variety of different looks.

3 Explain the procedure for cleaning and preparing a wig made from human hair.

4 Describe how you would put on a full wig and how it would be secured.

5 Draw a number of sketches to show hairstyles decorated with a range of ornaments.

</td></tr>
</table>

Chapter 9

PHOTOGRAPHIC HAIRDRESSING, DEMONSTRATIONS AND PROMOTIONS

Introduction

Promoting a business through photographic work, demonstrations and promotions is not solely for large or wealthy salons. The purpose of promotional work is to raise the salon's profile and increase turnover and can produce some stunning financial results. At its best, it will earn you the respect of your contemporaries (or competitors) and favourably impress existing and new clients. Before rushing into organising a photo-session or demonstration, you will need to plan the promotional activity carefully and match it to your identified business planning needs. This will mean making decisions about the most effective type of promotion to achieve your identified objectives and business targets. For example, is the objective of the promotion to increase sales of particular services, to attract new clients or promote a new salon image? You will also need to consider how you will measure the effectiveness of the promotion (meeting your targets). This may include monitoring financial targets and client appointments, conducting client satisfaction surveys and evaluating the success of the activity to identify its strengths and weaknesses.

The photographic session

Every day, thousands of photographs and transparencies hit the desks of trade and consumer magazines, and every day, several hundreds are returned, rejected or ignored. One of the most difficult challenges a hairdresser faces is producing the right kind of work at the standard required to be published by the press. Poor quality shots will not be published and will result in you feeling you are wasting your time and money.

Models

Choose models carefully since they are by far the most important factor. Do not try to do too many models in one session because limiting the number gives you time to get things right and vary the style and you will not get too tired either. As a guide, four models could be done in a whole day session while only two models should be done in a half day session.

Photographer

Once you have found a suitable model (or models), you should arrange for the photographer. It is worth investing in a professional rather than attempting to take the photographs yourself. Some photographic sessions may be able to be carried out on the salon's premises but usually photographers will have their own studio or know of one which is available for hire. You can find a specialist photographer through the Association of Fashion, Advertising and Editorial Photographers or the Bureau of Freelance Photographers. Often, the initial fee quoted is only for the photographer's time. Check if there are studio costs, lighting, heating, etc. to go on top. Also check on the cost of film, developing, and reprinting and ask for these details in writing.

Make-up artist and clothes stylist

It is also worth investing in professionals for the make-up and sometimes the clothes. Most photographers will be able to recommend make-up artists and clothes stylists with whom they have successfully worked in the past.

If you are choosing the clothes and accessories yourself, make sure they are not fussy (distracting from the hair) and are not creased. With accessories, the golden rules are 'less is best' and 'if in doubt, leave it out'. A clothes stylist will help you create the right image but this can prove costly. Some shops will lend you the clothes and accessories you need in return for a credit on the photograph. You may even be able to borrow clothes from friends.

Briefing and coordinating

You will need to thoroughly brief the photographer and make-up artist (and clothes stylist if you are using one) and discuss the effect you want to create and the 'feeling' you are aiming for. Do not leave this until the day because it will not give people sufficient time to think about lighting, backgrounds, colours, moods and textures. It is a good idea to appoint a person as the coordinator of the session. If you have different people organising different things, you will end up with different uncoordinated concepts.

The day before

Prepare the model's hair the day before the session (colouring, cutting, etc.) to save wasting valuable time and money on the day. You should have a clear idea of the types of styles you will be doing and have practised ahead so they are easy to do on the day. Draw up a list of all the things you will need to take with you and check these off as you pack them to avoid any last minute panics. Remember that you are unlikely to find a comfortable backwash at the studio and will probably end up wetting the model's hair using a water spray or the basin in the toilet.

On the day

Arrive at the studio (if that is where the shoot is taking place) on time or preferably a little early. If you are doing more than one look on a model, so converting the hair into different styles, always start with the lightest dressings and progress down to pomades for the heaviest work. The first photograph will always be a Polaroid so that those involved can check results and decide whether anything needs changing. Remember to look closely for any stray hairs and details that need adjustment such as width and height of the style. Listen to the photographer's suggestions and ask to look through the camera lens to make sure it is what you want. The photographer will shoot several rolls of film to ensure you get at least one good shot of each model. If you have only nine or ten shots to choose from, your chances of finding a perfect photograph will be slim.

Choosing the photographs

After the session, the photographer will give you a set of contact sheets. These are pages of the developed photographs which are set out in numbered strips and each shot will be only about 4 cm square so you may need to use a photographer's magnifying lens to see the detail of each photograph. The photographer may have already marked the shots that he or she thinks are the best. The photographer will need to be told which ones you want and to which magazines you will be sending them. Make sure you have the correct spellings of people's names for the credits.

Labelling the photographs

Before sending the photographs to the press, you will need to clearly label each picture stating the salon's name and the names and roles of those involved (i.e. hairdresser, photographer, make-up artist, clothes stylist, etc.). Also include a contact name and telephone number and a brief description of how the style was created. If you are sending a photograph, write on a label and stick this on the back of the photograph. Never write directly onto the photograph with any sort of pen because you will make impressions on the print which will make it unfit for publication. If you are sending a transparency do not remove it from its protective cover. Instead, attach it to a piece of paper (not by stapling through the transparency) which has the relevant details already written on it. Send the pictures in a hardback envelope and clearly write the words 'Photographs – please do not bend' on the front and back.

Tips for successful photographic sessions

Many people make the mistake of trying to be too arty, producing adventurous pictures that do not really work because they lack the experience.

Others fall into the trap of trying to copy something they have seen or liked, not realising that magazine editors are looking for originality. You are therefore advised to go for a clear, polished image which is good enough to be used on its own but versatile enough to blend in with others in a general hair feature.

Hairdresser

The hairdresser should have planned and practised the looks to be photographed and performed any technical services (e.g. perms and colours) and cutting before the shoot. To get the most of the session, the hairdresser should choose adaptable styles which can be converted from, say, day to evening looks on the same head.

Models

The models need to have very good skin (no lines or spots which will show up in photographs) and regular features. An attractive person will not necessarily be photogenic. Invest in a Polaroid camera to take snaps of potential models to check they photograph well. Also make sure the model's personality fits the types of photographs you will be taking and that they feel comfortable and confident in front of a camera.

Photographer

The photographer should have done hair photography before because it is very different from straightforward portrait shots. Ask to see their portfolio (a type of folder containing a selection of their best photographic work) before committing yourself to hiring them.

Make-up artist

The make-up artist will also have a portfolio of work for you to see. People who are not regular make-up artists may go overboard and try and do the make-up they have always wanted to try which may not suit the hair. Make sure the make-up artist understands the type of look and feeling you are hoping to achieve and that they are prepared to change an approach if the first one does not work. A good make-up artist will also be aware that one type of make-up does not always work for black and white and colour film alike.

Clothes/fashion stylist

The clothes/fashion stylist will be able to advise you on fashion themes for the following year and will arrange the hiring, borrowing or buying of the clothes and accessories to be used.

Lighting

The lighting is dictated by the type of hairstyle being photographed. The more aggressive the hairstyle and image to be projected, the stronger the lighting will need to be to accentuate the hair. Natural daylight can some-times work well but it will need to be strong enough to show the hair detail well. Tungsten halogen lighting used with a red head (a spotlight which heightens detail) gives a warm glow. Soft lighting with a flash diffuses the effect and softens the detail. Daylight with tungsten fill-in gives a hard, sharp image and is usually used for black and white photographs but if used with colour will give a green cast. This is good for 'mood' shots as it flatters the face and jawline by bleaching them out and can add shine to hair.

Backgrounds

The backgrounds which are generally best are the most simple. Floral backgrounds and glitter backing can be obtrusive and detract from the hair. Outside shots can be ruined if nobody noticed the pylon in the background that spoils the shot.

Costs

The costs will of course vary but you should allow approximately £2,500 to £3,500 for a full day session. The studio can cost anything between £300 and £2,500. Refreshments for the crew will set you back about £30. The make-up artist will cost in the region of £150 to £450 and the clothes/fashion stylist approximately £150 to £350. Professional model fees are usually based on an hourly rate and vary from about £50 upwards unless they are relatively inexperienced and are doing it for free in return for photographs for their portfolio and the press coverage. Remember that the stylist doing the work will be out of the salon (therefore not generating income from attending to clients) and there will follow-up costs for processing, developing and sending out the photographs to the press. It can be done more cheaply but do not skimp on the essentials.

Choosing models

Remember that attractive people will not necessarily be good models. Just because they have good features and skin does not always mean they will be photogenic. You have a choice of using professional models or selecting them from your clientele or other sources. Choose the models for their good complexion, even features, the type of hair (and hairlines) they have and their personality.

Professional models can be contacted through model agencies and they will have a portfolio and a 'Z' card. A 'Z' card is a professionally produced card (normally A5 size) which has a photograph of the model and lists his/her colour of eyes and hair, and measurements. If using professional models, you may need to hold a 'casting'. It is unlikely that professional models will allow you to cut or change the colour of their hair. Agree all professional model fees in advance and sign a model's 'release' form at the end of the session. If a hairdresser initiates a session intending that the photographs will be for editorial purposes only and then decides to use them for something not originally specified (say in a local newspaper advertisement), the model's payments may need to be renegotiated. This is because the model agency will demand that the model is paid the difference between the original fee, and what should now be charged for the extra things the photographs have been used for. If you are unsure about agreeing such contracts with model agencies, photographers and alike, do seek legal advice from a solicitor who has dealt with photographic copyright matters before.

If using clients as models, always take a Polaroid to make sure they photograph well. Some seemingly ugly people look terrific in photographs and the pretty ones just do not come across. You may be able to recruit models from your local college if you are unsuccessful in finding the right ones among your clientele.

Publishing your work

Now that the points about organising a photographic session have been covered, you will have a clearer idea of the standard of work needed if it is to be considered for publication. Never underestimate the value of a good photograph. It may do more for your business than you think. Before posting your photographs to the press, find out the name of the appropriate person to receive them by telephoning the editor's secretary. Write a covering letter introducing yourself and make sure your address and telephone number (including STD code) are mentioned. Be sure that every photograph is suitably captioned (details of the crew, how the style was achieved, and so on) using the methods described earlier. Photographs and transparencies may not automatically be returned (even if they are not used) unless requested. Check the procedure with the editor's secretary.

If you plan the session carefully and produce some good photographs which are published, you will have achieved an excellent means of putting across the salon's image and the satisfaction of knowing your work has been 'immortalised'.

Portfolio development

There are two types of portfolios. The type of portfolio put together by photographers, designers, session hairdressers, models, make-up and clothes/fashion stylists contains a good standard and cross-section of their work. Every picture needs to be professionally mounted and displayed with care and thought. The purpose of this type of portfolio (or 'book' as it is more frequently called) is to use it to show potential clients in the hope that they will like what they see and book them for future sessions. Obviously the work included in such a portfolio needs to be outstanding as advertising and promotion agents will see dozens of 'hopefuls' each week. As a session hairdresser, you will need to show the range of your skills by including pictures featuring simple and commercial hairstyles to more technical and avant-garde looks.

The other type of portfolio is used by those taking qualifications who are required to collect evidence as proof of their practical skills, breadth of experience, knowledge and understanding. Those readers taking NVQs/SVQs will already be familiar with how a portfolio is used to support accreditation and is a means of demonstrating your competence to assessors and verifiers.

Using photographic evidence in your portfolio

- Photographs should feature the candidate whenever possible to authenticate that the work was carried out by the person claiming it as theirs.
- The photographs should depict the *process* of the activity without going overboard. For example, if you were using photographic evidence to show your competence in completing a particular haircut, perm wind and styling technique, you should aim to include photographs which show the following stages:

photo 1	the 'before' shot (showing client consultation)
photos 2–3	cutting the hair
photo 4	the completed cut
photos 5–6	winding the perm
photos 7–8	the completed wind
photo 9	the wet result
photos 10–13	drying and styling the hair
photo 14	the finished result

- Each photograph will need to be carefully displayed and requires a caption to make sure the reader understands the significance of including the photograph.

Taking better photographs for your portfolio

It is a major disappointment to find that photographs did not develop as well as you had hoped or, even worse, not come out at all. You will need access to a camera and a flash as most of your work is likely to be taken inside, needing additional light. You can always play it safe and use a Polaroid camera which produces 'instant' photographs that develop before your eyes, but this can prove costly in the long run because Polaroid is relatively expensive.

Often, an otherwise good photograph is spoiled by the subject posing too hurriedly or by unwanted shadows and reflections. A three-quarter angle pose is much better than a full-face, square-shouldered photograph of the type used for police records and passports. Ask the model to look slightly past the camera rather than staring directly into the lens because even the curvature of contact lenses can reflect the flash. If you are using a camera which does not have a built-in flash, direct it so that it points up to the ceiling so that the light bounces off from above creating a softer light. Beware bouncing light off strongly coloured surfaces since the colour may tint your subject. Try to use a simple background and if possible, your subject should be at least 2 metres (6 feet) away from it to prevent shadows being cast behind the head. Never take a flash photograph directly into a mirror because it will result in a waste of a picture. If using a flash on a camera that does not have a zoom lens, try not to get too close to the subject to avoid 'bleaching out' all the colour and detail in the photograph.

Keeping clear records

When you receive your prints, always write the details on labels and stick these on the back of the prints so that you can keep track of which photographs you have and what they are for. Keeping a note of the photographs as you take them is useful. Making a record of each shot's print number, the name of the subject, and what the photograph is depicting will help you sort the photographs more easily, particularly if you are sharing the film with another person.

Dealing with the press

Getting editorial coverage in your local newspaper and trade and consumer magazines will put the spotlight on your salon and attract clients. Contacting the press takes little time and effort but can dramatically influence your salon's turnover and clients' perceptions of the business. Personal contact is a good thing and if you can persuade a journalist to meet you, then this initial meeting can be followed up with telephone calls and press releases. The initial meeting gives you the opportunity to introduce yourself, explain your news story and discuss future happenings and events which may be of interest. You will also learn the name(s) of the people you should deal with in the future. If you decide to pass on the responsibility of dealing with the press to another member of staff, always write to your press contact(s) to let them know this is happening.

Writing a press release

When writing a press release remember to focus on the who, what, where, why and when of the story and try to keep to one side of A4 paper. Only submit press releases which are genuinely newsworthy and of general interest. Always type press releases and use double line spacing and wide margins so that it can be more easily read and edited. Include the full names of people mentioned in the press release and a contact name and telephone number for any follow-up.

If you include a photograph with the press release, black and white prints are usually preferred and the full names of those featured in the photograph should be written on a label and stuck on the back of the photograph. 'Action' photographs always stand a better chance of being published than boring ones which show a line of people smiling sweetly at the camera. If you are able to include a local celebrity (such as a player from the local football team), this will increase your chances of publication.

Do not spend ages trying to think up a snappy headline for your press release because the journalists dealing with it will probably come up with their own. Despite your efforts you may be unlucky and find that the press release does not get editorial coverage. It may be that your news coincided with more important events (e.g. a local bank robbery) so there was no space available to include your editorial.

Journalists write copy in a 'house' style which is suited to their readership, so expect your press release to be altered accordingly. They also need to work to tight deadlines and it is unlikely that you will be able to see any edited copy before it is published. Most journalists will be irritated by such a request and may avoid contacting you in the future.

Inviting the press to an event

Invitations to the press to attend special events and happenings should be sent out at least three weeks beforehand and to a named person. Invitations should include an outline and timings of the event, and a map clearly showing the location. It is a good idea to have a visitors' book at events so you have a record of who attended. Always greet your guests and do not expect them to make their own introductions. If you (as the person inviting the press) are unable to look after your guests, delegate a person to do this on your behalf and to answer any questions they may have to help them with the writing of an accurate article. Journalists have a private life too, so do not be too disappointed if weekend or evening invitations are declined. You can always invite them to talk to you about the event during the daytime, offer them a cup of coffee and start building a good relationship.

Salon promotions

There are many ways of promoting the business of a salon which can be planned to achieve an overall objective (e.g. increase turnover across the board) or designed to promote a specific area of the salon's work. Here are a few examples of types of promotions.

- Giving each client who has a colour treatment a free home haircare product designed for coloured hair.
- Displaying a new product range and offering a discount.
- Organising a 'sale' on perms during a traditionally quiet period.
- Offering discounts to clients who introduce their friends to the salon.
- Having special children's discounts and events running during half-term school holidays and the week before school starts in September.
- Offering linked services – for example a free cut with every set of highlights.
- Working in cooperation with a manufacturer for a week to focus on a particular service and offering free consultations with your 'guest' from the manufacturer.
- Persuading all your female staff to wear nail varnish to promote your manicure service.

- Displaying show cards, products and showing a video to promote a particular range of products and/or service.

Any type of promotional work requires careful planning and should have clearly defined objectives which can be monitored and evaluated during and after the event. All staff should know about the promotion and the objectives to be achieved should also be explained. Offering incentives to the staff who will be involved will help induce enthusiasm for the promotion. Such incentives might be a prize or cash bonus for the most sales. You may need to order additional stock to cope with the demand and inform existing and new clients of the promotion by placing an advertisement in the local press, advertising on local radio, displaying a notice in the salon window and/or by distributing leaflets.

Demonstrations

Hairdressers are, in effect, demonstrating their skills every day of their working life on the 'stage floor' of the salon but formal demonstrations need careful thought and planning. The purposes of demonstrations will be either to train others or to promote salon services and/or individuals.

Whatever the size of the audience, or whether it is to train others or be used as a promotional tool, you will need to go through a planning process which will involve asking yourself the following questions.

What are my objectives?

This means identifying the purpose of the demonstration and deciding whether it is the most appropriate way of achieving your objectives.

Who is my audience?

Knowing your audience is important because you will be able to plan your demonstration according to the age, experience, background and language of those seeing your demonstration.

What will I be demonstrating?

You will need to decide what you will be showing your audience to ensure the demonstration is interesting enough to keep their attention. For example, some demonstrations are better if they include a mixture of models who are semi or fully prepared so that the audience can see a wider range of finished looks.

Where will I be doing the demonstration?

Always make sure you are familiar with the facilities available at the venue and pay particular attention to power points, lighting, sound, the staging and preparation areas (including seeing if there is running water).

If you are choosing the venue yourself, ensure that it is easily accessible for your audience and that refreshments and toilets are available.

When will I be doing the demonstration?

If you are not the only person doing a demonstration, make sure you know when you are due to perform by checking with the running order. Ensure your model knows the importance of being on time and always have a stand-by model in case of emergencies.

How much time will I need?

Do a run-through of the demonstration if you are not sure of how much time each stage of the demonstration takes. Usually, the time available will already have been determined by the running order of the presentation or the timing of the training session.

How can I ensure the audience can see what I am doing?

During a training session it may be necessary for you to ask your audience to move or gather around to see certain points and using revolving chairs and a special demonstration mirror (placed above the demonstration area) can be helpful. Asking your audience to move is not usually possible (or desirable) during a promotional event. Raised platforms and stages will help the audience to see much better and if the audience is particularly large, it is worth considering using video screens to transmit what is happening on stage at strategic points in the venue.

What will I need to say to support my demonstration?

Always plan what you are going to say to explain what you are demonstrating and remember to introduce your model by name. It is sometimes difficult to talk and work at the same time particularly if you need to use a microphone (to amplify your voice) which needs to be held. If you are using a compère, plan the questions he or she will ask you in front of the audience to avoid unexpected and embarrassing situations. If you are demonstrating in front of an audience made up of people who speak another language, you will probably be explaining what you are doing through an interpreter. Make sure the interpreter is familiar with hairdressing terms so that you can rely on that person correctly translating what you say. It is always worth learning a few words in the language of the audience. Even simple greetings and pleasantries like 'good evening', 'thank you for your attention' or 'hello, everybody, and welcome to our show' will be warmly appreciated.

How will I involve my audience in the demonstration?

If your audience is large, it is more difficult to involve them in your demonstration but you will still need to create a rapport with them. Always introduce your model so the audience feels it knows you both. If you are demonstrating to a smaller group of people in a training situation, make a point of asking them to look for particular things in your demonstration to keep them alert and interested. It may be worth asking them to make simple diagrams of what you are doing and stopping now and then to ask questions to check that they are following the demonstration. It may be appropriate to invite one or two people to come forward and 'have a go'.

What resources will I need?

Make a list of everything you will need for the demonstration including everything from the model to the tools and products you will need. Use your list to check things off to be absolutely sure you have forgotten nothing. Remember that if your model has never done anything like this before that you will need to talk them through what they will be expected to do, and what you will be doing, in order that they feel more confident in front of your audience.

How will I evaluate the effectiveness of the demonstration in meeting my objectives?

For a training session, you could evaluate the effectiveness of the demonstration (i.e. measuring what has been learnt) through question and answer, asking your students to repeat what they have seen and by setting a short test at the end. If the demonstration was a promotional activity and your objective was to increase the salon turnover, you may wish to consider distributing special vouchers which are redeemed against particular services or products when they are brought to the salon. If doing this, you would need to set up a system for monitoring how many of these vouchers are used which would indicate the number of clients visiting your salon as a direct result of the promotional event.

Tips on demonstrations

- Prepare in advance and ensure your model is fully briefed.
- Speak clearly, look at your audience as often as possible, and *smile*.
- Ensure your audience can see the demonstration.
- Invite your audience to ask questions and become involved as appropriate.
- Seek feedback and evaluate the effectiveness of your demonstration.

Salon displays

Displays in the salon can be anything from simple retail product displays to elaborate window displays to promote services, products, or in celebration of particular occasions such as Easter, Christmas and Mother's Day. Just as a shoe shop entices a customer into the premises by an attractive window display to buy a pair of shoes, salons can use the same principle to promote the sale of hairdressing services and products.

If your retail display area is prominently placed and inviting it will do the selling for you. Retail products are often 'impulse' buys, so follow the example of how supermarkets sell at their checkouts and display products at the reception where clients pay their bills.

There is a saying 'eye-level is buy-level' which is a reason why sweets and small toys are placed low-level at supermarket checkouts so they will be noticed by children. Place the faster moving products where they can be most easily seen and within reach. Try not to make a display so perfect that a potential purchaser is scared off from handling the goods in fear of spoiling the arrangement. Keep the products clean because dusty ones suggest they are old and not selling well. Retail research shows that most people are embarrassed about asking the price of something in case they cannot afford it, so a sale is lost. Price all items clearly and neatly using self-adhesive labels or a retail labelling device. It is a good idea to give the responsibility of displays to one person or to rotate the responsibility among the junior staff. In-salon competitions could be awarded for the best displays and ideas for promoting particular products and services. Table 9.1 lists dos and don'ts for displaying goods in the salon.

Table 9.1 Dos and don'ts for displaying goods for sale

Do display all of your stock as a large amount attracts more interest	**Don't** leave most of your stock in the stockroom where it cannot be seen
Do mark every product clearly with its price	**Don't** leave products unpriced; clients may be reluctant to ask you the price
Do make sure that the goods are easy to see and accessible	**Don't** have goods under lock and key as clients will be reluctant to ask you to take them out
Do make displays large to attract attention	**Don't** set up too many small displays as they have less impact
Do use your salon window and entrance area to let passers-by know that you sell retail goods	**Don't** miss the opportunity to exploit your salon frontage to its full extent
Do make displays attractive and change them regularly	**Don't** leave items in the window until they are faded, or use damaged items

One of the most important factors of all in retail selling is to get staff interested in selling products. This can be done in a variety of ways, including commission, profit-sharing for the whole salon and simply using the products in the salon.

Professional window display tips

- As with a hairstyle, the balance and shape of a display are important. Occasionally stand back from the display as you set it up to check that it is in proportion and well balanced.

- You can create texture in a display by the clever use of different back drops, fabrics and surfaces (e.g. silk, sacking, wood, glass, sand, sawdust) and 'props' such as dried flowers, stones, pottery, wrapped gifts and plants.
- Colours should be coordinated and consideration needs to be given to the occasion and time of year when choosing colours.
- If you are lucky enough to have spot lighting in the window, direct the lights so that specific areas are highlighted for maximum impact. Christmas tree lights can be very effective for some displays.
- Keep your display simple and eye-catching.

Revision Questions

1 What is the purpose of promotional activities?

2 How many models are you advised to use during a full day photographic session?

3 Who could you contact to find a specialist hair photographer?

4 Why are the first photographs taken always Polaroid ones?

5 How would you prepare prints and transparencies for sending to the press?

6 Make a list of the things for a photographic session which are likely to incur costs.

7 What is a professional model's 'Z' card?

8 By what other name might a session hairdresser's portfolio be called?

9 Make a list of the types of things which would be put into a portfolio of evidence.

10 Make a list of recommendations for using and taking photographs as evidence in a portfolio.

11 What are the key facts to be included in a press release?

12 Make a list of your ideas for promotional activities.

13 What would a hairdresser need to consider when planning a training demonstration to a small group of staff?

14 Make a list of recommendations for displaying retail products in the salon.

Advanced Questions

1 Imagine that you have been asked to organise a half day photographic session and find out the total costs of the following:

(i) studio and photographer

(ii) make-up artist and fashion stylist

(iii) professional models

(iv) refreshments for the crew

(v) film processing and printing

2   Explain a situation when it may be necessary to renegotiate a model's fee at a later date following a photographic session.

3   Write a press release about an interesting hairdressing event for a local newspaper. The press release should be no more than one side of A4, be typed, have wide margins and double line spacing.

4   Briefly describe a salon promotion in which you were recently involved and state how well it achieved your objectives. Include any changes you would make to the promotion to make it more effective.

5   Write a plan for a training session which will include a demonstration covering the following:

   (i)   Your objectives.

  (ii)   A summary of the backgrounds of your audience.

 (iii)   An outline of the actual demonstration.

 (iv)   The location and time of the demonstration.

  (v)   An indication of how long the demonstration will take.

 (vi)   A plan of the room and seating layout for the demonstration.

 (vii)   Notes which depict your explanatory talk during the demonstration.

(viii)   The questions you will be asking your audience or other ways it will participate.

 (ix)   A list of the resources you will need.

  (x)   How you will obtain feedback on your performance.

 (xi)   How you will evaluate how well you met your objectives.

acid: chemical compound that contains hydrogen ions and has a pH of less than 7.0. Acids close the cuticle layer of the hair.

acid conditioner: conditioner which has an acidic pH and helps restore the hair's natural pH.

acid mantle: layer of acidity maintained on the skin's surface. Gives the skin a slightly antiseptic property.

acid rinse: rinse containing a weak organic acid used to close the cuticle and to neutralise alkalinity.

activator: any agent that induces activity such as those used in acid perms. Also describes the products applied to permed Afro-Caribbean hair to nourish the hair and separate the curls.

aerosol: container (usually a cannister) in which the contents are kept under pressure and released by propellants. *See* CFCs.

aescalups: alternative name for thinning scissors.

Afro-Caribbean hair: hair of negroid origin which usually has a naturally tight curl formation.

albino: person whose skin and hair lack pigment due to a genetic defect.

alkali: chemical compound that contains hydrogen ions and has a pH of more than 7.0. Alkalis open the cuticle layer of the hair.

allergy: a reaction to contact with something, usually seen as a dermatitis on the skin.

alpha-keratin: hair in its unstretched state.

amino acids: small molecules that proteins are made of; in the cortex they help maintain the moisture balance.

anagen: first part of the hair growth cycle in which the hair is actively growing. It lasts between one and seven years.

analysis: examination of the client and the client's hair before a hairdressing service is performed.

anticlockwise: describes curl formation in a direction opposite to that travelled by the hands of a clock.

apocrine gland: type of sweat gland found attached to hair follicles in the armpits, pubic regions and around the nipples. The decomposition of this sweat by bacteria leads to body odour.

arrector pili: muscle attached to the hair follicle that causes the hair to stand up on contraction.

asymmetrical: not evenly balanced.

avant-garde: an image or look which is a forerunner of fashion.

backbrushing: roughing hair by brushing from points to roots to add volume to hair; the hairs entangle because the brushing action causes the cuticles to stick out.

backcombing: method of achieving support and fullness; the shorter hairs are pushed down towards the roots with the aid of a comb.

backwash: a basin in which the client's hair is shampooed. The client is in a reclined position so that the back of the neck rests in the special groove of the basin. It is much safer to use a backwash than a frontwash when rinsing out strong chemicals.

barrel curl: open centred pincurl.

barrier cream: waterproof cream used to protect the skin from chemicals.

basal layer: bottom layer of the epidermis where cells are actively dividing.

base: area of the scalp from which a mesh of hair is taken for setting and perming the hair.

beta-keratin: keratin in its stretched state.

bevel cutting: a technique of club cutting the hair so that slight graduation is created at the points.

bleach: product capable of lightening the hair.

blow-drying: using a hand-held hairdrier in unison with a brush, comb or the hands to dry and shape the hair.

blow-waving: using a hand-held hairdrier in unison with a comb to dry and form the hair into wave movements.

blunt cut: alternative name for club cutting.

braid: plaiting of hair using two or more strands.

breaking point (of hair): *see* tensile strength.

bristle: animal hairs used in brushes.

buckled ends: distorted points of hair caused by the incorrect winding when setting, blow-drying or tonging hair.

build-up: repeated coatings of colorant on hair shaft.

cape: wrap-round protective garment used to protect the client's clothes.

capillary: small blood vessel found between the arteries and veins; supplies the hair follicles with oxygen and nutrients.

catagen: second part of the hair growth cycle, the breakdown period, which usually lasts about two weeks.

cell: basic unit of life; the skin and hair are made up of a collection of cells.

cell division: the way in which a cell grows; a parent cell divides into two smaller copies of itself in a process called mitosis.

CFCs: abbreviation for chlorofluorocarbons. CFCs are propellants found in aerosols. They are harmful to the ozone layer, which protects the earth from ultra violet radiation from the sun. Banned in many countries.

chignon: type of long hair dressing.

chipping: technique of thinning the hair using scissors.

clip: clamp-like device used to secure the hair.

clippers: haircutting tools which can be either electric or mechanical.

clockwise: movement of hair in the same direction as the hands of a clock.

club cutting: cutting the hair straight across to achieve blunt cut ends.

coarse hair: hair fibre with a large diameter.

cohesive set: wetting, moulding and drying the hair in a stretched position as in the case of setting and blow-drying.

comb: tool used to part, dress and arrange the hair.

comb-out: use of a brush or comb to dress the hair into the finished style.

commercial: image or look which is recognised as being currently in vogue.

concave: surface that curves inwards; opposite to convex.

conduction: transfer of heat or electricity in solids by movement of atoms.

consultation: discussion which takes place between a professional and a client during which clients express their wishes and the professional gives advice.

convection: movement of heat in gases and liquids; warm air rises, cools and falls again, setting up a convection current.

convex: surface that curves outwards; opposite to concave.

cortex: central layer of the hair, consisting of bundles of fibres and making up the bulk of a hair. This is the part of the hair where chemical processes take place and where the natural pigment is found. This gives hair its strength and elasticity.

COSHH: Control of Substances Hazardous to Health.

counterclockwise: movement of hair in the opposite direction to the hands of a clock.

cowlick: strong area of hair growth in the opposite or an unusual direction on the front hairline.

cranium: bones of the skull which protect the brain.

creativity: ability of hairdressers to express ideas artistically through their work.

crest: raised part of a wave.

croquignole: winding the hair from points to roots.

cross-checking: process of checking one's work.

cross-linkages: bonds in the hair between cortical fibres.

crown: top part of the head from where the hair takes its direction of growth.

curler: alternative word for a roller used for setting or perming the hair.

curly hair: hair which is not straight; may be of Caucasian or Afro-Caribbean type.

cuticle: outer layer of the hair, consisting of several layers of overlapping scales. This provides protection.

cutting comb: straight comb with both wide and closely set teeth.

cysteine: amino acid containing one sulphur atom. Two cysteines are oxidised to form one cystine molecule during the fixing (neutralising) stage of a perm.

cystine: amino acid containing a disulphide bond, which is reduced by perm lotion to form two cysteine molecules.

damaged hair: hair which is porous, brittle, split, dry or has little elasticity.

dense: thick, heavy, abundant.

dermal papilla: collection of cells at the base of the follicle which is the source of hair growth.

dermatitis: inflammation of the skin as the result of being in contact with some external agent, e.g. perm lotion, shampoo.

dermis: second layer of the skin, containing nerves, blood vessels and connective tissue. Sometimes known as 'true' skin.

disentangling: removing tangles and combing the hair smooth, usually carried out with a wide-toothed comb.

disulphide bonds: strong cross-linkage in the hair formed between two sulphurs.

dry hair: hair that lacks natural oils (sebum).

eccrine glands: type of sweat gland found all over the body. The sweat consists of water and a little salt.

elasticity: ability of a hair to be stretched and return to its original length.

elasticity test: test performed by the hairdresser to assess the strength of the hair's internal structure, i.e. the cortex.

end papers: papers used to prevent buckled ends and distorted points during winding, usually when perming; can also be used when setting hair.

epidermis: outermost layer of the skin, consisting of five separate layers. Protects the body from physical damage and water loss.

European hair: type of hair found on people originating from Europe (Caucasians).

evaporation: process in which a liquid turns into a gas.

expansion: when something increases in size, usually on heating.

fantasy: describes looks or images which are extreme and imaginative.

feathering: alternative name for taper cutting.

fibrils: thread-like fibres found in the cortex; there are three types – protofibrils, microfibrils and macrofibrils.

filler: chemical preparation that equalises porosity by filling in the more porous areas of the hair.

fine hair: hair fibre that is relatively small in diameter.

finger wave: process of moulding the hair in a pattern of waves by using the fingers and a comb.

flammable: substance that will ignite or burn.

follicle: a downgrowth of the epidermis from which a hair grows.

free-hand cutting: cutting hair without holding it in place.

French pleat: hairstyle which is dressed so that the back hair is made into a fold.

frizz: hair having too much curl.

gel: thick oil-in-water emulsion used to style hair.

gland: tissue which produces a secretion, e.g. sebaceous and eccrine glands.

graduation: method of cutting which blends longer meshes of hair into shorter hair lengths.

grey hair: mixture of white and coloured hairs that gives the overall illusion that the hair is grey.

groove: hollow trough of a pair of curling irons or tongs.

guideline: the first cutting line which is made and followed throughout the entire haircut.

hair: form of keratin that grows from a follicle.

hair bulb: lower part of the hair root.

hair growth cycle: three-part cycle of a hair's growth: anagen, catagen and telogen.

hair growth pattern: direction of an individual's hair growth.

hairline: edge of the scalp where the hair begins.

hair shaft: the part of the hair that projects from the skin.

hairspray: fine spray used on dry hair to hold the hair in position.

hard water: water that contains calcium and magnesium salts, which will not easily form a lather with soap.

honing: sharpening the blade of a razor or removing damage to the blade edge.

horny layer: top layer of the epidermis, which consists of a lot of dead cells. Its main function is to protect the cells underneath from physical injury and water loss.

humidity: water in the air.

hydrogen ions: hydrogen atoms which have a positive charge because they have lost an electron. Found in acids.

imbrications of hair: the point where cuticle scales overlap.

induction: process of introducing people to the organisation which they have just joined.

infra red: type of radiation which is invisible and provides heat.

inversion: term used to describe the cutting of hair so that it is shaped inwards to form a concave or 'V'.

keratin: protein from which hair, skin and nails are made. It differs from other proteins because it contains sulphur.

keratinisation: hardening process of keratin during its growth and development.

kinky: very curly hair.

lacquer: originally derived from shellac; now made from water-soluble substances that 'stick' and hold the hair in place after styling.

lanolin: purified sheep's sebum.

lanugo hair: hair found on a foetus.

layering: method of cutting hair which reduces its length.

litmus: dye used to indicate whether something is acid or alkaline by a change of colour (acid = red; alkaline = blue).

male pattern baldness: type of alopecia caused by sensitivity to androgens. Can affect both men and women although it is more common in males.

mandible: lower jaw.

Marcel waving: technique of forming waves in the hair by means of heated irons.

medulla: innermost layer of the hair, consisting of hollow air spaces. It may not be present in some hairs.

melanin: black or brown pigment found in both hair and skin.

melanocytes: cells which produce the pigment melanin, found in the germinating layer of the epidermis.

membrane: semi-permeable outer covering of cells.

mesh: generally, a small, manageable amount of hair taken to make the work of the hairdresser more efficient.

mitosis: type of cell division where one cell divides to make two smaller copies of itself.

ml: millilitre; a metric unit for measuring which is one-thousandth of a litre.

Molton Browners: flexible foam-covered or cloth-covered 'rollers' used for setting or perming hair.

mousse: aerosol foam hairdressing product, usually in the form of styling or colouring foams applied to damp hair.

nape: lower part of the back of the head nearest the neck.

negotiation: process of reaching an agreement through discussion.

nerve impulses: electrical 'messages' sent to the brain along the nerves.

nervous system: network of nerves in the body that control the other body systems under the overall control of the brain.

neutral: having neither an acid nor alkaline pH reading: a pH of 7.0.

nucleus: the part of a living cell that contains all the genetic information.

NVQ: National Vocational Qualification accredited by the NCVQ; equivalent to SVQ.

occipital: bone that forms the back of the head.

on-base: placing a roller so that it sits squarely on its own base.

ornamentation: items used to decorate and enhance hairstyles, e.g. ribbons, flowers, beads.

outline: perimeter shape of a haircut, beard, moustache or sideburn.

over-directed: placing a roller so that it sits on the upper part of its base to produce maximum volume; also means positioning the hair during blow-drying so that maximum lift and volume at the roots of the hair are achieved.

papilla: source of hair growth, found at the base of the follicle.

perimeter: outside line of the hair.

pH: (potential of hydrogen); symbol for hydrogen ion concentration; a scale of numbers which indicate how acid or how alkaline something is.

pheomelanin: natural hair pigment responsible for yellow and red tones in hair; found in the cortex.

physiognomy: appearance and general characteristics of the head and face.

pincurl: strand of hairs organised into a smooth ribbon form and wound into a series of continuous and untwisted coils.

plait: intertwining various numbers of strands of hair to form a braid.

plane mirror: flat mirror.

pli: originates from 'mise-en-pli', a French term used to describe the setting of wet hair with rollers, pincurls and finger waves.

pointing: technique of thinning hair that is restricted to the ends of the hair.

porosity: ability of hair to absorb liquids, which is determined by the condition of the cuticle.

porosity test: test to check the porosity of the hair and thus determine the condition of the cuticle.

posture: how people arrange their bodies when standing or sitting.

propellant: gas contained in aerosols to force the contents out through a nozzle. *See* CFCs.

protein: a type of foodstuff made up of amino acids linked chemically together. Found in meat, fish and various vegetable sources. Needed for growth and repair of cells.

radiation: transmission of energy in the form of rays.

rake: comb-like attachment for hand-held blow-driers or high frequency machines.

record card: a means of recording information about clients and the services they are given.

reflection: occurs when heat or light hits a surface and bounces off. The image that is seen in a mirror is reflected.

refraction: bending of light rays as they pass from one medium to another, e.g. from air to water.

reverse pincurling: placing open pincurls in alternate rows, in clockwise and anticlockwise directions; produces a wave pattern.

root sheath: cells that hold the hair in the follicle.

salt linkage: type of linkage found in the cortex.

scrunch-drying: a blow-drying technique that involves grasping the hair to achieve curl and movement; ideal for increasing the hair's natural movement or creating more volume in permed hair.

sebaceous glands: oil glands attached to hair follicles which secrete sebum directly into the follicle to lubricate the skin and hair.

sebum: oily secretion of the sebaceous gland which helps lubricate and waterproof the skin.

sectioning: dividing the hair into separate parts or panels.

sectioning clip: used to secure sections of hair.

sharps: sharp objects which could puncture or cut the skin.

sharps box: special container used for the safe disposal of sharps.

shingling: using the scissors over comb or clippers over comb techniques to cut hair very short in the nape region.

spiral winding: winding hair from roots to points.

split ends: damage to the ends of the hair which results in splitting along the hair shaft. The scientific term is Fragilitis crinium.

stand-up pincurl: open pincurl which stands up from its base producing volume at the roots.

static electricity: term used to describe build-up of a charge on the hair, caused by friction when brushing or combing hair, especially when newly dried.

stem direction: the part of the hair that determines its root direction in setting.

sterilisation: complete destruction of all living organisms on an object.

strop: flat piece of leather used to maintain the edge of a razor.

sulphur bonds: bonds found in the cortex which are broken during perming and relaxing treatments.

SVQ: Scottish Vocational Qualification accredited by SCOTVEC in Scotland; equivalent to NVQ.

sweat: fluid produced by sweat glands in the skin, composed mainly of water with a small amount of salt. Its function is to maintain the body's temperature by evaporating and cooling the skin.

sweat gland: gland that produces sweat.

symmetrical: evenly balanced and proportioned.

synthetic: something produced by artificial synthesis in a laboratory or factory.

tail comb: comb, half of which is shaped into a slender, tail-like end, used when setting the hair.

tapering: removing length and bulk from the hair simultaneously using either scissors or a razor on wet hair.

technique: method of accomplishing a desired aim.

telogen: the third part of the hair growth cycle, the resting period, which usually lasts 3 – 4 months.

tensile strength: amount of tension that is put on hair, by means of a weight, that will cause the hair to break. A hair in good condition could support about 120 – 150 g before breaking.

tension: stress put on the hair by stretching and holding tightly.

tepid: slightly warm, lukewarm.

terminal hair: coarse hair found on the scalp and, after puberty, on other areas of the body (beard, under arms and pubic region).

texture: the 'feel' of hair; the quality of hair described as coarse, fine, etc.

thermostat: automatic device that controls and regulates temperature.

thinning: method of cutting which removes bulk without affecting the overall length of the hair, e.g. pointing.

tissue: group of cells and their intercellular substance that forms one of the structural materials of the body.

translucent: something that allows some, but not all, light to pass through it.

transparent: something that allows all light to pass through it.

trough: dip or hollow of a wave.

under-directed: placing a roller so that it sits on the lower part of its base to produce less volume at the roots.

vellus hair: soft downy hair found on the body.

vertex: top or crown of the head.

virgin hair: hair which has not been previously chemically treated.

viscous: thick and sticky (liquids).

visual aids: materials used to assist in the explanation and demonstration of concepts and principles, e.g. shade charts, photographs, slides, diagrams.

volatile: a liquid that has a low boiling point and so evaporates easily and quickly; e.g. setting lotion.

vulcanite: material produced by treating rubber with sulphur to increase resistance to heat.

water vapour: water in the form of a gas.

weave cutting: method of selecting strands of hair for cutting; a method of thinning.

white hair: hair that is colourless, containing no pigment.

wind: wrapping of hair around rollers, brushes, perm rods and the barrel of curling tongs.

Index